SCARS, SKELETONS, AND THE SECRETS THAT BIND US

PART I
~CAUSE AND EFFECT~

SCARS, SKELETONS,
AND THE SECRETS THAT BIND US

PART I
~CAUSE AND EFFECT~

KAY KARENZ

ISBN: 978-1-7376301-0-4 (E-book)
ISBN: 978-1-7376301-1-1 (Paperback)

Printed in the U.S.A
First Print – September 2021

DEDICATION

I dedicate this book to young girls and women who mistakenly believe that they are irredeemable. You may not have always made the right choices, but you didn't break any molds. Everyone has a past. The good news is that your mess-ups can be cleaned up. You can emerge from your experience wiser, stronger, and so much better than you were before. Never, ever let anyone tell you otherwise.

ACKNOWLEDGMENTS

First and foremost, I thank my heavenly father, my life-sustaining force to whom I owe everything. I know very well where I would be without Him. I would not have finished this book without His inspiration, encouragement, and the signs that I couldn't ignore. He often shook me up a bit to get me going, but everything finally came together. He deserves all the honor, glory, and praise for whatever good comes from what I have written. Thank you, Lord, for choosing me.

Thanks to my husband, Tony. Your gentle inquiries and subtle nudges always provide me with a special kind of motivation. Thank you for giving me space and time to let my creativity flow. You're my quiet anchor, the one who has captured me like no other. You are the true love of my life.

My son Stephen - I'm not sure why He did it, but God chose me to bring you into this world. From that special moment onward, you have been a source of inspiration for me in countless ways. But the most important one of all is the joy that came from being a mother to you. What an honor! I am so grateful for our amazing relationship. I love you, infinity + infinity.

My beautiful sister Kizzanne, whom I adore. There was a time when we had no control over our circumstances. We've experienced tragedy, separation, heartache, and betrayal. But through it all, our indomitable spirits have helped us survive. Your story is mine. Thanks for allowing me to share it. My love and admiration for you will always remain.

Rosa, my fierce, awesome daughter-in-law. You are my living, breathing vision board and constantly remind me that the "world is my oyster." The excitement you express about my aspirations means everything. I claimed you years ago, mi amor, and you are forever stuck like chuck!

LeShelle Moore - I can't thank you enough for agreeing to be my beta reader, checking in, and holding me accountable. Whenever I asked, you delivered without fail. What I love most about you is that you've never ended our conversations without asking, "Is there anything I can do to help?" You're one of my gems, and I hope you know how much I appreciate you.

Dawn Coleman - my editor and educator. You are one extraordinary woman. When I think about all that I have learned from you during this process, not just about writing but about life in general, "thank you" seems inadequate. You have helped me be a better storyteller, and I know that the fruits of your labor will pay off!

Thanks to my awesome sister-girlfriend Sheron for being in my life, my corner, and accepting me just as I am. The memories we have created always warm my soul. I love the bond and laughter that we share, and I love you! I can't hear "Freak of the Week" without thinking of you with a broad smile on my face.

Mady, my Chica - I am moving closer towards the dream I've shared with you for quite some time. It is about to come true, and you know where you're going to be, right? Thanks for our beautiful judgment-free friendship. But most of all, thanks for being you! Love you, girlie, girlie!

My Dear Di Di - Your kindness, generosity, and encouragement have blessed me in *so many ways*. You have always been one of my biggest supporters, and I appreciate you coming through whenever I need an on-the spot-editor. You'll always hold a special place in my heart.

Jackie and Sheryl - Long-lasting friendships are hard to find. But decades later, ours is still going strong! You ladies are uber fantastic, and so is our sisterhood. I am thankful for you, our weekly calls, and our discussions about everything under the sun. It amazes me that we can talk for hours and still not have enough time. I love you both dearly.

Gerry and Christine Beach - Everyone should be blessed to have friends like you. Thanks for being there during my Texas years. Gerry, you were a godsend. And Chris, kudos to you for letting me and so many others share your wonderful hubby. I will forever be indebted to both of you. Much love always!

Lucretia Jackson, my mama Lou - A long time ago, you asked me, "Why are you afraid of your success?" Your question and subsequent tough talks gave me the spark I needed to resume my writing which I have never forgotten. Thanks for keeping it real! You already know how much you mean to me.

Yolanda Hooks - you were the first to read a rough draft of my manuscript many years ago. I was nervous about your reaction, but as always, you remained calm, didn't raise your eyebrows, and made me feel at ease. I guess I was on to something because you stayed up all night plowing through those pages. Thanks for not shutting me down.

Acknowledgments

To Shirley Weatherley-Williams, Tracey Belle, Shirley Titus, and Margelee Hylton, my subsequent alpha readers. Thank you! Your feedback during the early stages of my writing meant everything.

Autumn Gill, my other incredible beta reader. Amid your super busy schedule, you still carved out time to read my manuscript. I truly appreciate you and your support.

Sonya Bryan - I am so glad that we met! I love your energy and our connection. Thank you so much for agreeing to work with me. This has been a wonderful collaboration, and I look forward to many more.

Linda McCallum-Byrnes - I was blessed to see you on July 14, 2021. Along with your sister Cathy Means, the enthusiasm you showed for my literary endeavors had me feeling on cloud nine. I had no idea that I would never see you again. May your beautiful soul rest in peace.

Last but certainly not least - I extend my heartfelt thanks to those of you who have encouraged me to write. Your positive affirmations inspire me more than you know.

Kay

Jeremiah 29:11

"For I know the plans I have for you," declares the LORD,
"plans to prosper you and not to harm you, plans to give you
hope and a future."

A MESSAGE FROM KAY KARENZ

Dear Reader,
Thank you from the bottom of my heart for purchasing this book. You have taken a chance on me, an indie author, and for that, I will always be grateful.

I began writing this story in 2008, shortly after an experience I had at church. One Sunday, while sitting in my usual spot on the 2nd level, I watched a group of young women stand in unison and respond to the altar call. During their walk towards the alter, I couldn't help but chuckle inwardly. A few wore skintight dresses, which they tugged at in a futile attempt to pull down to the middle of their thighs.

I furtively glanced at some of the mature congregants near me to see them shake their heads slightly in disapproval. These church folk, donned in their Sunday best, were not impressed. Then, as clear as day, I heard a voice say, *"If only they knew your story."*

On the way home, I thought about those girls and the mature congregants, which led me to reflect on where I was at that point in my life. Various scenes of things I had done and situations I had been in flashed through my mind. Yet, I had much to be thankful for. I had already learned firsthand the magnitude of God's goodness, despite the stain of my sins.

For days, I couldn't get the statement, *"If only they knew your story,"* out of my head. While I have always believed that my testimony was worth sharing, I preoccupied myself with how it would be received. I had no problem speaking to others who were going through similar predicaments. However, the potential fallout from divulging details in a book was unsettling no matter my calling. I was not prepared to answer the onslaught of questions from family and friends. Indeed they would focus more on determining which transgressions applied to me or them rather than the key takeaways. Also, though I hadn't broken any molds, I worried about being judged.

So I did what I always do when I am indecisive about something. I prayed and asked God to remove the desire to write this book if it was not His will for me. The exact opposite occurred. The seed that He planted continued to grow, I received confirmation to move forward via irrefutable signs, and thus my literary journey began.

Nevertheless, everyday life got in the way. With a demanding job that often had me getting home way past dinner time, I had just enough energy to take care of my husband, our home, and a massive fur baby.

But God is good! He blessed me with an opportunity that allowed me to focus on my passion according to His perfect timing. Now my first novel has been completed.

This true, coming-of-age story isn't for everyone, especially flawless individuals who have consistently exemplified perfection. On the contrary, it is for people who struggle with owning their truth and self-forgiveness. And book one of this series provides a cautionary lesson for all young girls. I'll explain further.

While spending time with my girlfriends, there were many instances when our conversations evolved into full-blown confessionals. With tears streaming down their faces, they shared some of their deepest secrets. As I divulged a few of mine, the relief of telling their story to someone without judgment was comparable to having a two hundred pound weight lifted off their shoulders. These imperfect beings were ashamed of their wrongdoings and held on tight to the albatross of guilt they carried. Instead of embracing the lessons learned, they fixated on their sins. There was no understanding of how their mistakes and trials could become blessings for others.

Then we have the judges. Those who have been through some things and have a past. Yet, instead of addressing pressing topics with young women on a relatable level, they condemn them for walking down the same path they took years before. These women choose to bury their wrongdoings, carry themselves with a misplaced air of superiority, and pretend to live exemplary lives, devoid of questionable circumstances.

Lastly, this book is for teenaged girls thinking about having unprotected sex or who are already sexually active. If the consequences of the main character's actions give pause for thought, then the right impact has been made.

Before I move on, I want to make it abundantly clear that I do not advocate teen sex, a pro-choice agenda, or abortion as a solution for unwanted pregnancy.

Some of you may question whether or not God intended for me to be this transparent. My answer is a resounding yes! He has demonstrated time and time again that His mercy and grace have no boundaries; that neither is limited to those who go to church and faithfully attend mid-week and Sunday services only. If I cannot be honest about my trials, how can I testify about receiving his agape love, mercy, and grace?

The focal point of this series isn't about the commonality between mistakes that we make. It is about life and should encourage you to look at certain aspects of yours with fresh perspectives.

Mothers, think about the daughters you are raising and ask yourselves these questions. Are you doing everything possible to prepare them for womanhood? How would they fare if, God forbid, you were taken away unexpectedly? Are you setting examples that demonstrate what it means to be responsible, self-sufficient, and self-loving individuals? Do you have age-appropriate conversations about relationships? If you aren't with their fathers, are you mindful of the men you allow in their spaces? Are there any unhealthy cycles that should be broken?

Fathers, do you fully comprehend the impact that your presence, or lack thereof, can have on the development of your daughters' confidence and self-esteem? Do you give them unconditional love so that they know to walk away when anything less is presented? How do you interact and communicate with the mothers of your daughters and other women in your family? Are you conversing respectfully or in a demeaning manner? These attributes, amongst many others, play a pivotal role in determining the women that your daughters will one day become.

In closing, I want the following to register: Even when we are at our lowest, God will never stop loving us or doing what is in our best interest. I was in my 40's when it dawned on me that during the midst of my ugliness, the blessings kept coming.

There was a period when I had so many good things happening in my life that I felt embarrassed. Imagine that! And God did all of this when I was least deserving.

Beloved, hold your head high. No matter what the masses may say, you cannot shock God. Trust and believe in Him. He has an incredible plan with your name written on it, and nothing can stop you from having what is divinely yours!

Peace and Blessings,
Kay Karenz

CONTENTS

THE BAD SPIRIT

"*So, He thinks she's worth saving. That she's a good girl who has made a few bad choices. That she'll learn from her mistakes and go on to live an exemplary life. Hah! Little does He know that I have her in my grip. You see, when I get into a mind, I can take over. What is dirty, ugly, and destructive becomes clean, beautiful, and all-encompassing. I can make anyone do my will, even when they know there'll be dire consequences for their actions.*

Everyone knows that forbidden fruit is the sweetest fruit. The Good One thinks He can speak to her heart, her conscience, her common sense. Not going to happen. She's already fallen. Oh! I may have some challenges. He's planted a few of His good spirit seeds. If I'm not vigilant, I can lose this one to the other side.

To prove my point, I'm going to put their precious Analia on a roller-coaster ride. Yes, indeed! Her life is going to be turned upside down. You may wonder what it is that I want. I'll tell you. I want her to become mine, all wrapped in my cloak of sin. I want to see her destroyed and of no use for good. I want her to lose the little faith she is starting to acquire. I don't want her to get to know Him. He says she was created in His image. What a joke! Her image is more like mine. Just like the many other lost souls on earth who know me so well.

I am going to wreak havoc on Analia. I will strike during her moments of weakness. She will succumb to temptation and never walk the straight and narrow path. I will take immense pleasure in watching her fail. I've got a unique plan for Miss Analia, and I might give some attention to her sweet baby sister too! The battle between good and evil has begun!"

THE GOOD SPIRIT

"*A*nalia is a special girl. She has been chosen for an assignment that will ultimately end with her being a light for many. This isn't evident now. But later, much later, she will come to realize that what she has been through was necessary.*

Analia's choices are questionable at times, but her heart is in the right place. As she navigates through life, you will meet a compassionate, caring individual: one who shows genuine concern for others. I have work to do, but she can be saved despite her iniquities and the many times she will succumb to sin.

She is about to embark on a tumultuous journey. You see, I have a master plan, even though it may not be revealed for many years to come. Nevertheless, I'll be there with her through the good and the bad. Nothing will happen to Analia that I do not allow.

I am watching her, alone in a hospital far away from home. Physical pain torments her body while she fights a swirl of emotions that fill her with feelings of abandonment, remorse, and shame. She tries to figure out how she got there. But deep down inside, she knows the answer.

There will come a time when you or someone you know will be able to relate. The details of your story may be different, but the implications will be the same. Everyone is susceptible to sin. No one is immune. At any time, you can fall and build an ugly past; commit transgressions that you hope will remain hidden, even after your last breath is drawn."

"Whose house is of glass, must not throw stones at another."
George Herbert, 1651

PROLOGUE

October 15th, 1980

As Analia lay in her hospital bed in the dimly lit ward, she fought hard not to scream. She tossed and turned and tried to get into a comfortable position, but her efforts failed her. Waves of intense cramps came furiously without respite. Nothing could be done to ease the searing pain in her abdomen. Nothing had prepared her for this torture; the price she had to pay for a moment of pleasure.

Analia silently questions herself. *God, what am I doing here? How did I end up in this place? How could I have been so stupid?* She knows that what is happening is real but still can't believe her predicament. She should have listened to her uncle when he told her to stay away from Kevin. He warned her repeatedly that she was too young to be in a sexual relationship. She had her whole life ahead of her, he often explained. But more importantly, she would see that this boy who claimed to love her only wanted one thing. And that was what she had between her legs.

Her uncle, Rendall, was a womanizer. She saw him use and abuse countless women. And because of this, his words fell on deaf ears. His warped way of child-rearing caused Analia too much pain for her to take heed to his caution. So why would she listen to a man who had upended her life, treated women like cattle, and had no loyalty to anyone but himself? Because this time, he was right. She should have paid attention.

Analia knew precisely when she messed up. The date was June 5th. She usually walked to school with her friend, Sydney. On that morning, when they got halfway there, Analia pretended that she had forgotten an assignment that needed to be handed in during her first-period class. She told Sydney to go on without her and that they'd meet up later that afternoon.

She turned around and headed back in the direction from which they had just come. Three blocks away, Analia caught a mini cab and took a twenty-minute ride to Brandy's apartment in Starrett City, where she planned to spend the day with Kevin. Brandy was a fling of Rendall's. She adored Analia, and the feeling was mutual. They developed a close, sisterly relationship. One that was so special, she allowed Analia and Kevin to stay in her home when they wanted to "see" each other.

They had met at Brandy's many times before. Still, as she settled in the back seat of the old Toyota Tercel, the fear of being discovered lingered in the background. But she couldn't pass on the opportunity to be with her love. The desire to be with him pushed any reservation to the back of her mind. Knowing what would occur, Analia should have delayed her visit for another week. A few months earlier, she started using the rhythm method to predict when she would ovulate. According to her calendar, she was ovulating. Now was not a good time to have sex.

However, Analia never said "No" to her heart. When Kevin told her that he "needed some," the reference turned her on. He never said he loved her; just that he "needed some." His innuendo made Analia feel special and emboldened her to take risks that she had no business taking at the tender age of sixteen. Thus, against her better judgment, she went to see him. Stupid! Just stupid to the nth degree!

She attempted to be responsible. Two years prior, Brandy introduced her to Encare, a vaginal contraceptive insert. She didn't condone sexual intimacy amongst teens. But knowing that the two lovebirds would do it despite her warning, she thought it best that Analia use some form of protection.

On the afternoon that she had bought several boxes of Encare for Analia, Brandy made her read the instructions on the back of the box, which stated:

> **At least 10 minutes prior to intercourse: remove the protective wrap and insert Encare into the vagina (see diagram on package insert). Each Encare insert gives you one full hour of protection. May be used with: condom or diaphragm for added protection. Before use: read all directions and special warnings on this package and the insert inside.**

She even opened one of the boxes, retrieved an insert, and gave that to Analia to read as well. Then she explained how the spermicide worked.

"It's going to melt, and when Kevin ejaculates, it will kill his sperm before they enter your uterus." Brandy had given her ammunition to prevent an unwanted pregnancy. However, the most effective form of contraception would have been to abstain from sex. But things had already gone too far. There was no turning back.

Brandy usually left her apartment shortly after her and Kevin's arrival. Luckily, she always had errands to run or someone to visit. On that fateful day, she departed shortly before nine-thirty. Then Analia and Kevin retreated to one of her spare bedrooms.

Although they'd be alone for a few hours, time was of the essence. Analia needed to be back on her side of town by two-thirty. They hurriedly undressed then got under the blanket on the twin bed. Analia liked the limited space; it forced them to stay joined to each other.

As Kevin lay on top of her, they kissed each other deeply. He slipped his finger inside of her and masterfully teased her clit until she covered him with her juices. Analia felt something powerful stir between her legs as they turned up the heat between them. She reached for his penis and drew circles around it with the tip of her forefinger. Upon feeling a little pre-cum, she wrapped her fingers around him and began to move her hand up and down his throbbing member. He was rock hard; she was dripping wet. They were ready to start one of their marathon sessions.

Analia reached for her bookbag on the floor by the side of the bed. As she retrieved two inserts, Kevin turned to her and said, "Babes, we don't need that. I want to feel you."

She paused for a minute and looked at him. "Kevin. You know this is the week that I can't do it without using something. I'm ovulating."

"I promise, I'll pull out," he said as he stroked her body. Against her better judgment, she caved in. Analia dropped the insert on the floor and wrapped her arms around him. He entered her swiftly with one thrust.

**

Analia put her head against the railing of the hospital bed, and for a split second, the cold steel gave her momentary relief. Just as quickly, however, the pain returned and became even more intense than before. What little bravado she holds on to starts to dissipate. Between the onslaught of contractions, she begins to cry.

As she glanced around the ward, Analia espied other girls that occupied at least a dozen beds. She heard some of them moan and cry out in pain. The sounds troubled her. But she couldn't be like them. She couldn't afford to show any signs of weakness. She was alone and had to be strong for herself. However, no matter how hard she tried, there was no stopping the tears that ran from her eyes and into her hair. A combination of shame and remorse enveloped her as she thought about her current situation; sixteen years old and having a late-term abortion, which could have been avoided.

Analia remembered how she froze in a mild state of disbelief at Kevin's reaction to the news of her pregnancy. She never imagined he would ever turn his back on her. They experienced quite a few trying times together, making it hard to understand exactly what had changed. Analia had sacrificed so much to be with him, and he knew this.

Kevin chuckled when she told him that she was pregnant. His exact words were, "Well, you know I can't do anything for you." Unfortunately, the very same thing that she had been warned about is what happened.

The nurses and doctor on duty began making rounds to check on their patients. Analia could hear curtains being drawn around the other beds as the medical staff performed their examinations. She silently prayed that her ordeal would soon be over.

Although the doctor kept his voice low, Analia could hear murmurs. "Anytime now." "Just call when you feel the need to push." "Your daughter still has a long way to go," were some of the comments she heard.

Analia was surprised at the number of white girls on the ward. Since they weren't seen walking on the streets with their swollen bellies or at Planned Parenthood Centers, many believed them to be good and unspoiled; that they didn't have unprotected sex, which would result in pregnancy. Not like the black girls in the hood. Analia now knew that this notion was a fallacy; they did it just like other teens.

There was something else that surprised her. Every last one of the white girls on her ward had support. She looked at the women sitting in chairs next to their beds, gently stroking their arms, giving them pats of reassurance while they waited for their babies to pass. They were lucky. At least those girls didn't have to go through this ordeal alone while locked in the most unbearable pain imaginable.

Analia watched through tear-filled eyes as the staff approached the bed next to hers and the familiar sounds of an examination ensued. Stacy, the young girl who had been given her saline injection about fifteen minutes before Analia, moaned and groaned. She gritted her teeth and said she felt as though something was getting ready to happen.

"I can't hold it! Please help me! It hurts! It *hurts*!" she screamed.

One of the attending nurses drew the curtain back slightly, ran towards a cart, and returned with a metal pan. Analia could barely see what was happening through the semi-sheer curtain that divided their beds. However, she heard Stacy scream out again in pain and then heavy panting. A flurry of activity ensued, followed by the words that she hoped to hear soon.

"It's over now. You'll be going home shortly. We're going to help you get cleaned up."

One of the nurses remained with Stacy while another proceeded to leave with the doctor to check on Analia. While waiting for them to get to her, Analia also felt something happening "down there." It was as if all the cramps she had been having during several hours had knotted together and become one big ball of pain.

By the time the doctor and his nurse reached her bed, Analia lay on her back with her legs spread wide open. He lifted the thin cover sheet and examined her. As fire raced through her lower region, Analia struggled to breathe.

The nurse ran towards a cart, grabbed a metal bedpan, and said to Analia, "Try to raise your hips sweetheart, so that we can place this under you." The agony was intense. She could barely follow the nurse's instructions. Almost immediately, Analia felt the ball magnify to a new level, and everything froze in time for a few seconds. She had just given birth to a dead baby.

The doctor looked at her from his position at the bottom of the bed. He removed the pan and handed it to the nurse. Analia didn't see what was in the pan, nor did she want to. She just couldn't bring herself to ask the doctor to let her see "it."

She had already started the process of detaching herself from the awful experience that she had just gone through. Her mind shifted to preparation for her departure. Terri was scheduled to return at eleven in the morning to pick her up. She had a deadline to meet that could not be missed. If all went well, they'd make it back to Brooklyn with a few hours to spare before Uncle Rendall arrived to take her home. Analia thought about the homework assignment that she still had to complete and hand in on Monday. She also wondered if anyone at school would notice anything different about her. Her thoughts were all over the place.

She didn't hear any words exchanged between the doctor and the attending nurse, nor anything said to her. The assistants helped her move to the edge of the bed while they changed the pads. She laid back down per the nurse's instructions and didn't say a word. She was filled with an emotion she couldn't quite name. Empty. Disillusioned. Disgusted with her entire being. An epic failure.

The clock on a wall across from her bed displayed the time: 11:45 p.m. Analia didn't know the names of the doctors or nurses who attended to her, but she knew how long she had been in labor. She knew that she had delivered her baby nearly seventeen hours after receiving a saline injection.

Her dirty deed had been done. Now, she just wanted to go home and leave Lincoln Hospital with its dimly lit ward and beds occupied by pregnant teenaged girls having late-term abortions.

Any abortion is awful, but saline terminations are the worst. Analia had messed up on two fronts. First, she had unprotected sex and fell pregnant. Second, instead of addressing her predicament (as soon as she had an inkling that pregnancy had occurred), she waited until it was too late to have an abortion via dilation and curettage. Analia carried a fully formed baby, and because of her irresponsibility, she chose to deny that child a right to live.

Some say that "What is done in the dark will be revealed in the light." That's true. No matter how hard you try to hide the skeletons in your closet, they will escape. They'll expose themselves in some way, shape, or form. Each skeleton is tied to a mistake or a secret. Something that you hope is never revealed. But this is not how life works. At least not for Analia.

There are three facts that she would learn the hard way. That there is a consequence for every action, you can never be at peace as long as there are skeletons in your closet, and October 15, 1980, would come back to haunt her in more ways than one.

Chapter 1

THE HOOK UP

Life's a bitch, and then you die. Since I am alive, doing well, and have much to be grateful for, I guess the verdict is out on the dying part. Still, there is no denying the fact that one would do well to expect the unexpected. It is not a matter of if, but when fate will throw a few twists and turns designed to either make or break you.

I've been through some stuff. Yet, I count myself lucky. I have a fighting spirit, created from the love and discipline given to me by my parents. A spirit that sustained me when I encountered insurmountable challenges. To understand how I got to where I am today, I need to take you back to the beginning. We must start there because you need to see how circumstances can change in an instant. And before you know it, life's thunderstorms can envelop you in their midst.

My mother, Veronica, was born to Oliver and Clarinda Walton on December 7, 1943, on the Caribbean Island of Barbados. When she was two years old, my grandparents immigrated to Trinidad with their daughter and firstborn son, Errol. The Walton family lived in Trinidad for sixteen years. During that time, my grandmother gave birth to three more sons, Lloyd, Rendall, and Keston.

Veronica grew into a beautiful young woman. She was five feet, six inches tall, fair-skinned, and didn't have a single blemish on her face. Perfectly shaped eyebrows highlighted her large, light brown eyes. Her lips were plump and had a distinct natural liner. She usually straightened her long hair and styled it into a ponytail with bangs. Veronica didn't have the thick, curvy body type that most West-Indian women are known for. However, her other physical attributes made up for the small butt, skinny legs, and narrow hips, which she inherited from her mother.

In the summer of 1962, my grandparents immigrated again. This time, they moved to London, England, with my mother and her youngest brother, Keston. Errol, who was twenty years old, had received a scholarship to attend the University of Wisconsin in the United States. He had already been gone for over a year. Lloyd and Rendall, ages sixteen and thirteen years, were left behind with neighbors. Oliver and Clarinda assumed it would be easier to set things up and get established without their entire household in tow. They took Veronica and Keston with them and planned to send for their other sons to join them a year or two later.

My grandparents settled in the borough of Kensal Rise, in northwest London. The homes in this neighborhood were large, Edwardian structures with several rooms available for rent. With easy access to public transportation and shops nearby, Kensal Rise appealed to those looking for a decent place to live. All of the homeowners were white. Fortunately, most were not narrow-minded and refused to allow the racial discord in other parts of the country to stop them from renting to black people.

Shortly after her arrival, my mother connected with some friends from "back home," and they quickly introduced her to the London nightlife, 1960's style. Fetes (parties) and Lymes (get-togethers) were common around their neighborhoods. One night, they took my mother to one of these main events where she met a man who would later become my uncle.

Along with his parents and four of his seven brothers, Carl Edmonds had also recently immigrated from Trinidad to London. He was five feet nine, handsome, had almond brown skin, curly black hair, and an infectious laugh. He had a lean body and walked with a slow gait, giving his imaginary audience time to check him out. Carl sold hash and weed and made many acquaintances from all walks of life and of different ethnicities. His flat was the place to be on a Saturday night.

While attending her first party at Carl's place, my mother saw a picture of a fine man hanging on the living room wall. She told Carl she wanted to meet him.

"So, you want ta meet Victor eh? Yuh lookin' fuh trouble or what? Ah doh tink yuh ready fuh any of de Edmonds men yuh know," he responded in a combo accent that included both their British and island tongue.

"I ain't say all ah dat Carl. Ah just want ta meet him. You carryin' on as if ah say ah want ta marry de man. Anyhow, you sure he ready fuh me?" my mother replied. They both laughed. A few hours later, when he arrived at the party, she met the man in the picture.

Victor Edmonds was a fine, mocha-complexioned specimen. He was toned with long muscular legs at six feet three and not an extra ounce of fat on his body. His dark brown eyes were deep-set with lashes that were long for a male. Victor styled his hair in a neatly groomed buzz cut. His forehead was high, a physical trait he shared with his siblings. He had a square jawline, and his sexy full lips curled to one side when he smiled.

He thought it was a sign of good luck when he learned that the woman who had eyes on him had the same first and middle names as his mother. Veronica and Victor quickly developed feelings for each other. Two months after meeting, they moved into a flat of their own, located at 171 Harvest Road, in the same neighborhood where my grandparents lived.

Chapter 2

A MYSTERIOUS DISAPPEARANCE

While things were moving along nicely for the new lovebirds, the relationship between Clarinda and her husband deteriorated. Oliver Walton was considered a pretty boy. With his fair skin and straight, light brown hair, which he wore parted and swept back on one side, he could pass for white. His almond-shaped eyes were dark and framed with long, curly lashes. Most women found him irresistible.

My grandfather slept around and physically abused my grandmother. He spent many days and nights away from home and left her to take care of the household and Keston. Although my mother knew that her father was no good, she still adored him, and he had mutual adoration for her.

Oliver wasn't keen on his darling Veronica moving out on her own with a man she had just met, but he rarely came home to keep her in check. Whenever he decided to bless the family with his presence, arguments and fistfights ensued. Keston did his best to tune them out. However, there was one incident when everything spiraled out of control. It was the reason I never got to know my grandfather.

As told via the family grapevine, my grandmother, Clarinda, had had enough of her husband's infidelity. She decided to seek love elsewhere and began having an affair with a neighbor who lived in the same building as her family.

One evening, when my grandfather had been gone for several days, and Keston was at a friend's house, my grandmother invited her lover into her home. One thing led to another, and in her quest for the attention she craved, Clarinda threw caution to the wind. She and Rudolph made their way to the bed, which she occasionally shared with my grandfather, and began to make love.

***

Oliver returned home unexpectedly. Clarinda and her lover did not hear him enter the house, nor did they hear my grandfather open the bedroom door. After gazing upon his wife and neighbor in the throes of passion, he walked silently into the kitchen and returned a few minutes later. It was not until Clarinda felt Rudolph collapse on top of her that she realized something had happened. My grandfather had stabbed him in his back. As she attempted to move Rudolph's dead weight off her and slide from under him, Oliver stabbed her twice in her shoulder.

Keston, who arrived home shortly after my grandfather, entered the bedroom he once shared with my mother. Thinking his parents were having another one of their epic fights, he ignored the screams. However, this time, my grandmother's cries sounded a little different. He also heard an additional, *familiar* voice. It sounded like their neighbor, Rudolph, who seemed to be in distress. He opened the bedroom door slightly and could see his father holding a knife. Streams of blood dripped from the blade onto the carpet. He quickly closed the door and sank to the floor.

My grandfather didn't know it at the time, but both my grandmother and her lover survived their stabbings. However, thinking he had just killed his wife and Rudolph, Oliver fled the scene, and the police issued a warrant for his arrest.

Several weeks later, a passerby found a pair of pants and a shirt on a bank by the Thames. The clothing had gotten hung up on a small boulder. He searched the pants pocket and found a wallet containing two pounds and an identification card belonging to Oliver Walton. The young man reported his findings to the police, who informed my grandmother.

After making her way to the police station with my mother, Clarinda confirmed that the clothes and ID belonged to her husband.

Everyone assumed my grandfather committed suicide and left his garments where they would eventually be found. After speaking with Keston and learning about what he had witnessed, my mother blamed Granny for the chain of events that led to my grandfather's disappearance. From that moment on, the two women had an estranged relationship. My grandmother did everything she could to gain back her daughter's love and respect. But it took several years before they had even the slightest semblance of a mother-daughter connection.

No one ever saw my grandfather again.

Chapter 3

FIRST BORN

Two years later, my mother became pregnant. Although I wasn't planned, my dad called me his love child. He often told me that he didn't think my mother cared deeply for him. But none of that mattered. He was in love with her and the child they conceived together.

By the young age of twenty-three, my father thought his messed-up life was already over. He was heavily involved with gangs, spent most of his time smoking hash, and reveled in many drug-induced activities. However, the fact that he would have a baby changed his perspective on life and motivated him to become a responsible adult. He now had a reason to continue living. Even if he were no good to himself, Victor Edmonds was going to do all that he could to be an exceptional father.

My dad worked as an aircraft parts technician, a fancy name for a stock clerk, which provided a steady income for his household. My mother, an excellent seamstress, worked at a fur factory, sewing coats, and matching hats. To help make ends meet, she also made outfits for relatives and friends on the side.

On February 6, 1964, all six pounds, ten ounces of me arrived safely. From the moment Victor laid eyes on me, his heart was mine. According to everyone who knew my dad, no one ever loved a child more than he loved me. I was his world and the only person who loved him unconditionally.

From infancy, I was injury-prone. According to the family, when I was nine months old, my mother asked a friend to babysit me while she went shopping. It was during the wintertime, bitterly cold outside, and she did not want to take me with her.

When she picked me up a few hours later, I screamed and cried more than usual. However, my mother thought I fussed that way because I wasn't used to her friend. She didn't know that something was seriously wrong with me until we got home, and she attempted to change my nappy.

The tights that I wore would not come off quickly, and when she tried to pull them down, I screamed even more. When my mother finally made some progress, she was shocked to discover what looked like nasty open sores on my legs. Our family doctor's office was only a few minutes from our house, so she rushed me over there for him to examine me. During his examination, he determined that I had second-degree burns on my legs, seven in all. Due to the nature of my injuries, Dr. Schaeffer notified the police to investigate the incident.

Two policemen were assigned to our case. They went with my mother back to her friend's house to find out what happened. This woman, whom I will refer to as "The Scorcher," was ironing some clothes on a coffee table. Her doorbell rang, and not thinking, she put the iron down on the floor where I crawled around. While she talked with her visitor, I got tangled up in the cord, and the iron fell on my legs.

Now you know I must have screamed my little cherubic ass off. However, the witch never once thought to take me to the hospital. Instead, she dressed me in a clean outfit and waited for my mother to pick me up. When she arrived, "The Scorcher" acted as though we had a typical day. Once the details of the accident were disclosed, my mother tried to beat the crap out of that woman. The police almost arrested her.

Victor was upset about my accident. He wouldn't let my mum hear the end of it, and there was tension between them for weeks. His older sister, Joyce, lived a few blocks away, and he couldn't understand why my mother didn't have her babysit me instead of "The Scorcher." He insisted that I would never have been burned while in Joyce's care.

***

I had many more accidents and a near-death experience by the time I was six. While learning to ride a bike in daycare, I lost my balance and fell on a gigantic flowerpot. I cut my chin and had to get three stitches. I still have an ugly scar to this day, which ended my modeling career before it started.

One afternoon, while walking down the stairs in our flat, I slipped, busted my lip, and had to get another set of stitches. I have a permanent bump on my lower lip to remind me of that mishap. However, the worst accident occurred when I took sleeping tablets and almost died.

My favorite place to visit was my Uncle Carl's home in Ladbroke Grove, which is like Harlem in New York City. He was married to my Aunt Dora, and they had two children, Colin and Lorraine. I was close to my cousins and loved them dearly. I loved them so much that I would happily go along with any mischief they got into.

My parents and I usually went to Uncle Carl's on Saturday afternoons. On this day, when we arrived, my cousins and some of their neighborhood friends were downstairs in their bedroom hanging out. When we got bored with wrestling and pillow fighting, Lorraine, the eldest at twelve years old, came up with a brilliant idea. She decided that we should play "doctors and nurses."

Everyone agreed, and they chose me to be the first patient. Before the game started, Lorraine said, "Just a minute, let me go and get some medicine. I'll be right back." When she returned, she had a handful of tiny yellow pills in her hand and told me to take them before I had my "operation." Colin, who had a puzzled expression on his face, said, "Lorraine, those are Mum's sleeping tablets."

Lorraine looked at him and yelled, "Shut up, Colin! These are Smarties!"

I knew very well that what she gave me didn't even look like Smarties. But she was my older cousin, and I had to follow her instructions. I took a few of the tiny pills and put them in my mouth before getting off the "operating table." These Smarties were bitter and tasted nasty, but I didn't care. I ate them as ordered by "my doctor" and waited for everyone else to have their procedure. The next patient, Colin, was told to take the same medicine as me.

Colin and I were the only ones stupid enough to take those tiny yellow pills. Since I cannot recall what occurred after I ingested them, I'll tell you the story the way my father relayed it to me.

***

We left Uncle Carl's flat about two hours later. By the time

I got home, I was already in a deep slumber. At around eleven o'clock, my parents realized that I had been sleeping for several hours, which was unusual. My mother tried to wake me up several times by gently nudging, then shaking me, but to no avail.

Before long, my eyes started rolling up in my head, and my body began to shake uncontrollably. My dad called our neighbor, Bruce, and asked him to take us to the hospital.

We arrived in less than ten minutes. After being quickly admitted, the medical staff asked my parents several routine questions.

"Was she sick earlier in the day?"

"Has she taken any medication?"

"Does she suffer from any illnesses?"

My parent's response was, "No," and they told them that I had always been a healthy child with no medical problems.

My father became visibly upset, but Veronica remained stoic. Instinct prompted my dad to call Uncle Carl to determine if any of the other children at his house had fallen ill. My uncle told him that Colin was in a deep sleep and had been taken to a hospital in their neighborhood. He also mentioned that Lorraine came clean about us taking some of her mother's sleeping tablets.

Of course, she did not admit to giving Colin and me the drugs. And no one knows why my uncle didn't call my parents immediately after learning about what we had done. In the end, the doctors at the hospital finally understood the cause of my semi-coma. The nurses pumped my stomach, and eventually, I came around.

Chapter 4

CATHY ANN

The last major accident occurred when my father's sister, Aunty Annette, took me to their sister Joyce's home for a visit. Of the two aunts I had on my father's side, I least favored Joyce. However, I never passed up the opportunity to spend time with Aunty Annette or see my cousins.

My mother was selective about who she allowed me to spend time with. But Annette was her sister-in-law and best friend. And although she didn't have a close relationship with Joyce, she knew how much I loved being around her children. When Aunty Annette asked if I could go with her to Joyce's house in Wembley, she agreed to let me go.

I remember being excited about the alone time that I'd have with Aunty Annette. However, I had reservations about being with Joyce for any length of time. She was a mean old heifer whom I had good reason to dislike.

Unlike Aunty Annette, Joyce had an unshapely, stocky figure. Everything about her was thick: from her nose, right down to her limbs. She wore her hair in a short afro and didn't wear much make-up. Her light, melanin-deprived, almost translucent skin made her look like a ghost. Although she and Aunty Annette had the same parents, they could not have been more different in looks and personality. My grandmother, Veronica's eldest daughter, resembled her. Aunty Annette favored her father, granddad Cecil.

Wembley was different from Kensal Rise. It was more like the countryside and not as noisy or heavily populated. The houses in the neighborhood looked like two-story cottages with quaint gardens in the front. The air had a spring-like fragrance to it, and there was plenty of space for children to run around and be carefree.

My aunt was married to Harold, a pleasant man with a mellow personality. They had four children, Cathy Ann, James, Melvin, and Collin. Aunty Joyce gave her son the same name as her nephew, Colin, who lived in Ladbroke Grove. The only difference between the two names was the spelling. Although Uncle Carl had given this moniker to his son first, Joyce didn't see anything wrong with doing the same for hers. *Who does that?* The family should have known something wasn't quite right with her based on that crazy decision.

What I disliked most about going to Joyce's house was that she treated me like a stranger. On second thought, strangers would have been shown more hospitality. The heifer often put me outside in their backyard like a disobedient pet, while she gave her children biscuits, chocolates, and other delicious treats.

She also soaked burnt toast in water and gave me several glasses to drink throughout the day. This was known as a "cooling" in Trinidad, a concoction that was supposed to cleanse your blood. Purging is good for one's body, but I doubt that I was overloaded with toxicity at five years old! Surely her children needed purging as well, yet they were given fruit juices and fizzy drinks. No burnt toast soaked in water for her precious babies.

Joyce never liked me and did not attempt to convince me otherwise. She hid her true feelings around my parents, but whenever they left me in her care, she made it abundantly clear where I stood.

My parents were none the wiser about Joyce's mistreatment of me. Had either one known, I do not doubt in my mind, that they would have dealt with her ass accordingly.

Although I had a close, loving relationship with my father, I never told him about his sister and her preferred method of dealing with me. I guess I had an irrational fear of what would happen if I "snitched" on an adult.

***

In addition to Joyce's witchy ways, there was only one other inconvenience that I'd have to put up with whenever I visited her family; my cousin Cathy Ann's constant scratching in the middle of the night. She suffered from severe eczema and attacked her skin with a vengeance until the affected areas bled.

Being the only girl among her siblings, I shared Cathy Ann's bed when I spent the night at their house. Since I was a light sleeper, I lay awake most of the night while she tore at her arms and legs. I felt sorry for my cousin because she just could not seem to get any relief. The more she scratched, the more her skin itched, and the poor girl usually ended up crying. She was a pitiful sight to see.

Amidst all this scratching, Cathy Ann was the first person I allowed to touch me intimately, albeit in a childish way. She was also the first person I ever got busted doing something "nasty" with.

We always slept head to toe. But on the night we got caught, Cathy Ann decided to sleep at the same end of the bed as me. I had been sleeping on my side when she wrapped her arms around my stomach, then pulled me towards her at some point during the night. Suddenly, she started to push up against me, and I pushed back towards her. I was five years old, and she was seven. We didn't know what the hell we were doing, but we didn't want to stop either. Before I knew it, I could hear Cathy Ann remove her panties.

Without warning, the bedroom door opened, but we were too busy with our shenanigans to notice - and we sure as hell didn't see Aunty Joyce walk in the room. She pulled the blanket off us and shouted, "Cathy Ann! What yuh tink' yuh doin'?" We were both startled and afraid because Joyce looked pissed.

"Nothing, Mummy. Analia and I were just playing," my cousin answered timidly. I could see my aunt's nostrils flaring.

"Why yuh sleepin' with no panties on?" she barked. Cathy Ann gave a lame excuse about being hot. I knew Aunty Joyce didn't believe her. However, the thought of anything else going on would have been too much for her to handle. "Go ta de other end of de bed an' stay dere!" she barked again.

Cathy Ann scooted down to her spot while I held my breath and braced for my beating. It never happened. Instead, Aunty Joyce stomped out of the bedroom and returned about half an hour later to make certain we were not on top of each other again. Luckily, we weren't.

We got busted, but that sure did not stop Cathy Ann and me from humping on each other whenever she came to my house to visit.

Chapter 5

STITCHES AND PINS

On the morning of our trip to Wembley, Aunty Annette picked me up at nine-thirty. While on the way, she made sure that we stopped at a shop to buy my cousins some sweets. I chose the ones I knew they liked and couldn't wait to give them their treats. My parents instilled the importance of sharing with my family and friends. Even as a young child, I enjoyed giving things to people just because it felt good.

We arrived at Joyce's house safely. All four of my cousins greeted me warmly. After giving each of them a bag of sweets, I walked over to my aunt and hugged her. She squeezed me tight and tried her best to act as though she was happy to see me. I knew better. As soon as she got a chance, her mean streak would emerge. I had to give it to her. The heifer knew how to give an Oscar-winning performance when playing the role of a loving aunt.

"Analia, yuh growin' up so nicely. Yuh look just like yuh father side of de family," she fawned. "Annette, she could pass fuh yuh daughter more an' more every day."

"Ah know. Dat is what everyone does say," Aunty Annette replied with a proud smile.

For a moment, I felt as though the heifer and I made a connection. But common sense prevailed, and my guard went back up just as soon as I let it down.

The weekend went by quickly, and I had a great time with my cousins. I didn't have to drink any burnt toast water, and I got the same snacks as everyone else. With her sister nearby, Joyce was on her best behavior.

On the Monday before our departure, Aunty Annette visited a friend who lived about forty-five minutes away. Instead of going with her, I chose to stay at home with Cathy Ann.

My cousin and I spent most of the morning watching television. Once our favorite shows ended, we played outside in their backyard. We got the brilliant idea to climb an oak that was in the middle of the yard, something neither one of us had ever done before. And even though Joyce forbade us to do so, the defiant bug took over our common sense.

Halfway up the tree, Cathy Ann and I argued about who could climb the fastest. She gave me a playful push which caused me to lose my footing.

I landed on the ground with a heavy thud and felt all the air rush out of me. I'll never forget the shock of falling so hard. My right elbow felt like it was on fire. I tried to let out a scream, but it was as if I had become mute. I couldn't even breathe for a few seconds. I finally managed to catch my breath, turned my arm around to look at my elbow, and saw that it was split wide open to the bone. I noticed a broken bottle next to me on the ground, and pieces of the same glass were stuck in my flesh. Crying hysterically, I rushed into the house in search of my aunt.

**

I found Joyce in her bedroom, sitting in front of the mirror on her dresser, combing her hair. Between deep sobs, I said, "Aunty Joyce, Cathy Ann pushed me off the tree! Look at my elbow!" Even though she heard the distress in my voice, the heifer did not acknowledge me.

"Analia, move from me! Yuh can't see dat ah busy?" she asked with annoyance in her voice. As I started to walk away, she must have caught a glimpse of my blood dripping on her beige-colored carpet as it ran down my arm. "Oh my Gawd, lemme see!" she shrieked. She took a look at my elbow and freaked out.

"Cathy Ann, what happen ta Analia?" she asked in a panicked tone.

"I don't know. We were climbing the tree in the backyard, and she slipped," Cathy Ann replied nervously.

"Ent ah tell yuh not ta climb that tree? Yuh is a blasted girl! Leave dat nonsense ta yuh brothers! Look at yuh cousin elbow! What de hell ah suppose ta tell Veronica and Victor?" she yelled.

Cathy Ann, who anticipated getting a spanking, began to cry. Joyce grabbed a towel from her linen closet and tried to stop the flow of blood coming from my elbow. When it became apparent that she couldn't stop the bleeding, she took me to the hospital.

I screamed loud enough to wake the dead as a doctor placed pins in my elbow and stitched me up with no anesthesia. In all of my 1,825 days on earth, I had never felt pain like that before. The procedure hurt like hell! The attending nurse kept feeding me lollipops, thinking that sweets would calm me down or ease my discomfort. But all I wanted was my dad. I wanted to go home. I wanted to get away from the heifer Joyce and her daughter, who pushed me off the oak in their backyard.

When Aunty Annette returned later that evening and saw my arm in a sling with my elbow bandaged, she was concerned.

"Oh gawsh! Joyce, what happen ta Analia elbow?" she asked her sister. While waiting for Joyce to reply, she pulled me into a warm hug and asked if I was okay.

Naturally, in Joyce's version of the events, there was no mention of how she initially reacted to my injury.

When Aunty Annette and I were alone, I told her the correct version. I also told her about Aunty Joyce giving me nasty stuff to drink and putting me out on the balcony while she gave her children sweets.

Aunty Annette called my parents and told them about the accident. They came to get me the following day. I never went to Aunty Joyce's house again, and Annette didn't speak to her sister for months.

Joyce wasn't the only member of my dad's family that I didn't like. My fraternal grandparents lived approximately twenty minutes away from us, in Harlesden. Granny Veronica was a delicate-looking, fair-skinned woman. The most prominent thing on her was her nose. It had the same kind of flare as Aunty Annette's. She wasn't fun to be around. Her cold personality and firm voice belied her dainty appearance. Granny Veronica hardly ever smiled or interacted with her grandchildren. None of us enjoyed being around her. My parents and I saw her three or four times a year at the most, which suited me fine.

On the contrary, her husband, my grandfather Cecil, was a sweet man. He reminded me of my father. Although he had a darker complexion, they strongly favored each other. Grandad Cecil always had a smile for my cousins and me and spoke gently. You wanted to hug him, sit on his lap, and let him read to you, or just talk to you about anything in general. Grandad Cecil never failed to offer one of his cheeks for us to peck on it. In return, he gave us a couple of pennies to buy sweets.

My paternal grandparents were always in separate rooms. I rarely saw them eat together, watch television together or speak to each other. At the time, I didn't understand this arrangement. But when I became older, everything made sense.

In addition to his two sisters and Uncle Carl, my dad had another brother named Winston, whom we rarely saw. He lived in Northolt, London, and was called "de coconut" as he was black on the outside but white on the inside. In other words, he didn't associate with "his" people. The rest of my uncles: Vern, Harlen, Anders, and Felix, lived in Trinidad.

Chapter 6

COSTLY SWEETS

A s a youngster, I was well taken care of. Some would even go as far as to say that I was spoiled. However, if they knew the discipline I received from my parents, especially my mother, they'd agree that I deserved all of my toys, fabulous clothes, and birthday parties.

Veronica Edmonds loved to whip an ass. The spankings I received back then would land her in jail today. She made it clear that she only needed to tell or ask you to do something once. My mother would not repeat herself, especially when she wanted you to clean up any mess you made or to put something back in its proper place. She refused to negotiate with *any* child, hers, or anyone else's. As a matter of fact, she rarely negotiated with anyone, adults included.

Everyone has received a beating that they have never forgotten. I received mine for a simple misunderstanding that had everything to do with my mother and nothing to do with me.

I attended Chamberlaine Primary School, which was a few blocks away from where we lived. Every day, my mother walked me to school before she caught her bus to work. On the morning of my most memorable "cut tail" as West Indians called it, she walked with me to the school entrance and handed me a twenty-pence piece, which was a lot of money in 1969.

"Analia, dis is yuh lunch money for de week. When yuh give it ta yuh teacher, she'll give yuh back some change. Make sure yuh put de change in yuh money belt and doh spend it yuh hear meh?"

I nodded my head to show that I understood, but that form of acknowledgment was unacceptable. "Doh nod yuh head. Answer meh when ah speak to yuh."

"Yes, Mum. I'll bring your change back," I replied.

"Alright, go on ta school an' ah will see you later."

Veronica rarely showed affection, so we did not kiss or hug "goodbye" as we departed. Come to think of it, I don't remember her ever hugging me or even smiling at me. I'm sure she must have done this when I was an infant; at least I hope so.

What I do remember was her constantly disciplining me with commands of "Speak when yuh spoken to. Doh interrupt me when ah talkin' an' when you do, say excuse me. Doh sit between big people. Doh ever lemme catch you askin' anyone fuh sweets or money. Chew wid yuh mouth closed! No one should have ta see what yuh eatin'," and so on. She was tough and scary to me.

When I started school, my mother had a flexible work schedule, which allowed her to pick me up at the end of each day. However, on the afternoon of my infamous ass-whipping, our landlady, Elsa, met me at the school gate. She had been asked to do the honors, as my mother felt unwell.

***

On the way home, we stopped at our neighborhood corner shop, and Elsa bought me some sweets. When I arrived home, my mother was waiting for us at the front door of the three-story home that we shared with two other families. We went inside our flat on the first floor, and Elsa went upstairs to hers on the second.

I put my school bag on the kitchen table, and just as I was about to sit down, my mother asked, "Analia, how was yuh day?"

I didn't answer right away because my mouth was full of Jelly Babies, my favorite sweets. "Good Mummy," I said in a muffled voice.

"Where meh change from de lunch money ah give yuh dis mornin'?" she asked.

For a moment, I didn't know what to say because I couldn't remember what she was talking about. Then it dawned on me that my teacher had forgotten to give me my change. "Mum, Miss Jenkins didn't give me any change."

"What yuh mean she didn't give yuh any change? Who give yuh dem sweets yuh eatin'?" she asked. I could tell she was getting pissed, and in response to her rising temper, tears started forming in my eyes.

In Veronica's mind, the tears that threatened to spill indicated my guilt.

"Aunty Elsa gave them to me," I replied.

"Analia! Yuh know damn well yuh use de change from your lunch money ta buy dem sweets. Ent it?" she inquired harshly.

"No, I didn't spend the change. Aunty Elsa bought me the sweets," I said in a shaky voice as my tears started to flow.

My waterworks did not have the effect I'd hoped they would. "Go an' bring yuh Sunday school bag!" she yelled. I did as I was told and watched in fear as my mother removed the straps off my little plastic bag, pulled me to her, and started to beat me mercilessly. "Ah will not," *swish!* "have yuh lying," *swish!* "ta me" *swish!* "De next time," *swish!* "ah tell yuh," *swish!* "not ta spend" *swish!* "my money" *swish!* "ah mean it!" *swish!* "Doh spend," *swish!* "my blasted hard-earned money!"

I screamed so loudly that Elsa finally came downstairs to find out what was going on. "Veronica, what yuh beatin' Analia like dat for?"

"Because she have ta learn not ta lie!" my mother shouted. She told Elsa that even though she warned me not to spend the change from my lunch money on sweets, I went ahead and did so anyway.

"Yuh know how friggin' hard I have ta work for dat money?" she asked Elsa.

"Veronica, yuh wrong. Her teacher must be forget ta give her de change she had fuh her. Ah sure she will get it tomorrow. In any case, is my money dat buy dem sweets fuh Analia. She ain't spen' your money."

My mother looked at Elsa and said, "Well, she does lie too blasted much anyway!"

Elsa rolled her eyes and turned to me. "Analia darlin', doh cry. You'll be alright." Then she fixed her gaze on my mother. "Veronica, yuh does be a little too hard on dat child. I know yuh want her ta grow up right, but yuh can't beat her fuh every little thing. Gawsh, man!"

Veronica remained silent. Not because she was afraid of Elsa. She realized that she had gone too far and gave me a beating without just cause. Elsa mumbled something under her breath about my mum being crazy, walked out of our flat, and went back upstairs.

Instead of my mother apologizing or hugging me to make me feel better, she got a tissue and wiped my face rather roughly. While I continued to cry, she told me to change into the regular clothes she had laid out on my bed. She also announced that we were going to my Uncle Carl's house to meet my dad.

On the way to Ladbroke Grove, Veronica stopped at another corner shop and told me to choose whatever sweets I wanted. This was her way of apologizing. To this day, I can still remember that pink pocketbook with the cracked plastic straps and what it did to my little butt.

Chapter 7

ELECTRA

I once heard that some of the unwarranted ass whippings you received as a child were deposits for the future transgressions you would deserve a beating for later in life. I guess you could say I started my savings account at an early age.

I realize my mother wanted me to be raised up and not "dragged up," as the Caribbean folks say. While a few of her actions were justified, there were times when she went overboard. Another beating that I remember took place when she was pregnant with my sister. On this occasion, I had the pleasure of having someone else share my pain.

My grandmother had her youngest child, Orlando, at forty-three. This didn't sit well with my mom. Clarinda already had a three-year-old grandchild. The idea of her mother having a baby so late in life embarrassed Veronica. I cannot say that I blame my mother because many people couldn't hide their surprise when she introduced Orlando as her brother and not her son.

Orlando had been spending the week at our house to give my grandmother a little break. On the evening of our shared beating, my mother had an appointment with her obstetrician. My father was working overtime and wouldn't be home for a few hours.

I overheard her ask Elsa to keep an eye on Orlando and me while she went to the doctor. As my mother was about to leave, she looked in on us and said, "Ah going ta de doctor now. Make sure yuh pack away all of these toys before ah come back. I'll be home at six o'clock. Analia, watch de clock. Doh lemme find dis place in a mess when ah come back. Otherwise, you and Orlando will find out."

Orlando and I returned to our playing. We did not watch the clock as Mum instructed, and we lost track of time. My mother returned home, peeked in the living room, and did a quick scan of the scene before her. Then closed the door without saying a word. A few minutes later, she returned holding one of those old-school pink Avon hair brushes with the large, white plastic bristles.

My mother walked over to Orlando, grabbed him by one of his arms, and tore into his butt with the hairbrush. When she finished waxing his ass, she started on mine. Just as she raised her hand to give me the last stroke, my dad walked through the front door.

"What it is they do dis time?" he asked my mother.

"I doh know when dese blasted children will learn ta listen ta me. If Analia tink fuh one minute she goh ignore me when ah tell her ta do something, she have a next ting comin'," she replied.

My father looked at me and shook his head as if to say, "*When will you learn not to get on your mother's bad side?*"

"Analia, why yuh doh listen ta Mummy when she speaks ta you?" he asked as he picked me up and hugged me. At the sound of his tender voice, I cried harder. How does a five-year-old communicate that she lost track of time and forgot to put away some toys? Was that beating necessary? Hell no!

My grandmother picked Orlando up later that evening. Now being the baby of the family, he was spoiled rotten and hardly ever received discipline from Granny. When she found out about his whipping and saw evidence of it by the welts on his fair skin, she got enraged.

"Veronica, you can't be beatin' children all de time fuh every little ting. Yuh gone have dese dem frighten a you!" she yelled in her Bajan accent. She mentioned "children" but was referring to Orlando. I don't think Granny cared much whether I was the one getting the belt or the brush.

My mother didn't give a damn. When in her care, minors were expected to obey her rules.

"Eh heh? Well de next time he's in my house an' ah tell him ta do someting', he go tink twice about ignoring me," she retorted.

***

Veronica Walton was adamant about keeping children in check. My father didn't like unruly kids either, but he was a gentle disciplinarian. Even though he could be strict at times, I never doubted his love for me. I received spankings from him as well. However, deep down inside, I think it hurt him more to punish me at all. Dad always followed through on his promise to "get his belt" if I misbehaved. However, he also took the time to explain the reasons for his actions.

He repeatedly told me, "Analia, jus' because ah love you, dat doesn't mean ah wouldn't put meh hands on you. If ah tell yuh not ta do someting once, daddy warning yuh. If ah have ta tell yuh again, ah goin' ta be mad. And yuh know what dat means, right?"

A special bond existed between my father and me. I protected my relationship with him, and I didn't want anyone coming between us, not even my mother. I'm not sure how my parents had any personal time together. Even though I had my bedroom, I slept in their bed until I was six years old. I remember sleeping between the two of them with my arms under each of their heads as pillows. My little limbs ached with pain, but I refused to move them.

At times during the middle of the night, I would feel my father ease up off my arm and slide me over to one side of their bed. I pretended to be asleep, but through partially opened eyes, I watched as he got on top of my mother and started to move in a weird way. Eventually, I heard what I now know to be the sounds of their lovemaking and subsequent orgasms.

Shortly afterward, my dad returned to his spot on the bed, and they eventually fell asleep. I, on the other hand, stayed awake, trying to figure out what the hell it was that I had just witnessed. If "*it*" made my mother feel good, I didn't want them doing whatever "*it*" was anymore!

Sure enough, whenever they tried to make love, I pretended to be in the middle of turning in my sleep so I could face them. My dad gently turned my head in the opposite direction, but I didn't stay in that position for long. Finally, it got to the point where they'd let me fall asleep in their bed and, once I was out cold, they put me in my own. The Elektra complex indeed existed in our household.

Chapter 8

ANNETTE

I loved Aunty Annette more than my mother. Everyone outside of our immediate circle thought I was her daughter because we looked so much alike. Out of all her nieces and nephews, I was her favorite. She tried not to show any partiality towards me but couldn't help herself.

Aunty Annette was a petite, five-foot-four-inch beauty, with a figure shaped like a Coca-Cola bottle. She had the same mocha complexion as my father and a small beauty mark on the lower left side of her chin. Her shapely and muscular calves, acquired from constantly wearing high-heeled stilettos, popped out when she walked. Her hair was pressed and worn in a short pixie cut, which perfectly framed her beautiful face. The only flaw in her features was her flaring nostrils. However, this imperfection did not deter men of every race from flocking to her. You couldn't pay men to stop pursuing Annette Edmonds.

My aunt came to our flat every Friday after work unless she was ill or had a date. At five-thirty pm, with my mother closely watching, I walked or rode my bike to the red-letter box at the end of our road to wait for Aunty Annette to appear. She always gave me a bag filled with my favorite sweets upon her arrival.

Many of my father's friends, including Indians and white men, pursued Aunty Annette. Indian Trinidadians were known to stick with their kind, but even they fell for her. If she happened to be at our flat when they came over for a Lyme, they'd openly flirt with her. I'd see the looks of appreciation on their faces as she entered a room and often heard them say, "Aw gawsh girl. Yuh lookin' real good" or "Annette. Gimme a chance nuh? Lemme take yuh out. We go have a good time." She'd laugh them off and never showed interest in her would-be suitors as far as I knew.

I remember one evening, she took me with her on one of her dates. She had been going out with a white man named Raymond, who seemed nice enough but whom she didn't have deep feelings for.

I'm not sure what started their heated conversation, but as we drove over a bridge, Raymond put his car in park, turned to my aunt, and said with desperation in his voice, "What do you want me to do, Annette? Do you want me to kill myself? I'll bloody well do it if you leave me!"

My aunt nonchalantly responded, "If yuh want ta kill yourself, go on an' do it. No one stopping' you."

Raymond realized that his theatrics garnered zero points from her. He decided not to jump off the bridge. Instead, he stood against his car, held his head in his hands, and bawled like a baby. As young as I was, even I knew that his display of emotion was pathetic.

Aunty Annette did not get out of the car to console him. She remained seated and stared straight ahead while he had his mini-breakdown. When Raymond finally pulled himself together, he got back in the car, took us home, and that was the last I saw of him.

***

For a short time, Aunty Annette dated my mother's older brother, Errol. I suppose he was good looking. His eyes were light green with specks of gold in them. He had a high forehead with a widow's peak, like his mother's. Uncle Errol alternated between wearing his hair in a medium-sized afro and cornrows. He favored tight-hugging shirts with loud and colorful geometric patterns. He was a bit too much for me.

I didn't like Uncle Errol because he was too flashy. He spoke like a Yankee and made exaggerated moves when he danced. Moreover, he held my aunt's undivided attention, which was a "no-no" in my books.

When Aunty Annette went on a date with him, my face puffed up. When he asked her to braid his hair, my face puffed up. If she sat on our sofa with him instead of the loveseat with me, my face puffed up. If they engaged in any activity that didn't involve me, my face puffed up. I stayed puffed up for the duration of his stay.

Everyone laughed at my reaction to Uncle Errol being around Aunty Annette. Eventually, my mother stopped my antics by making it clear that I was a child and needed to behave like one. She also told me that she wouldn't tolerate me being rude to my uncle.

Chapter 9

DADDY'S GIRL

They say that girls marry their fathers. I suppose fathers are the first to show their daughters true love and how their future mates should treat them. My dad lived up to that expectation every day of my young life.

I recall with amusement an incident that I had with a neighbor of mine. After bathing, getting my hair pressed, which my father hated, and being dressed to the nines, I went outside to play. The other children who lived on our street didn't like how I stood out. They thought I showed off, and to be honest, there were times when I wished my mom dressed me down. This never happened. Veronica was proud of her family and loved putting them on display.

My neighbor, Giovanni, and I were close and often played together. One day, we had a spat. He punched me in my nose, causing it to bleed profusely. The sight of all the blood scared me more than anything else. I ran to my flat as fast as possible and rang our doorbell. My father answered the door. He did not expect to see blood all over my face and clothes. A look of anger mixed with concern replaced his calm expression from just a moment prior.

"Analia, what happened?" he asked.

Through my sniffles and hiccupping, I said, "Giovanni punched me in the nose." Victor, who only had on a pair of boxers, didn't think to put on pants or a shirt. He grabbed me by my hand and stormed towards Giovanni's house.

We arrived a few minutes later. Instead of ringing the bell, my dad pounded on the front door. Gio's father, Mr. Sasso, answered with my soon-to-be-ex friend hiding behind his legs. When my father saw how scared he was, some of his anger dissipated. However, he still had a few choice words to say.

"Listen ta me. If dat boy ever hit my chile again, ah goh deal with him on meh own terms," he warned.

"Calm down, Victor. Children play and fight every day," Mr. Sasso replied.

My father frowned. "Eh heh? Well lemme tell yuh someting. If yuh chile make dat mistake wid mine one more time, yuh go fine out!"

Victor glared menacingly at Gio's father, who stared back in disbelief. He looked as though he wanted to say something else. Instead, he kept his mouth closed. My father grabbed my hand once again, and we returned to our flat. That incident changed my friendship with Gio. We didn't call for each other as often, and when we did, we weren't as carefree as before.

***

My father and I often went on outings together. Except for work, I didn't want him to go anywhere without me. I tagged along during visits to Uncle Carl's flat or when he stopped at Ladbrokes to place bets on horse races or the off-license to buy his Guinness.

Before leaving, Dad would always ask the same question. "Analia, yuh have ta use de toilet?"

Sometimes, I'd answer truthfully. However, I often lied for fear of him getting impatient and leaving me behind. "No Daddy. I don't have to use the toilet," I replied, knowing fully well that I had to pee.

One time, we walked to the train station, and just as he approached the window to pay for our tickets, my tummy started feeling like it was about to bust. I hopped around from one foot to the other and squeezed my legs tightly together in a feeble attempt to keep from peeing on myself.

Before long, I couldn't hold it in any longer. I gave up the good fight and let that warm golden liquid flow and form a puddle right where I stood. What a relief! My dad was too through.

"Analia, didn't I ask you before we left the house if yuh wanted ta use de toilet? What is wrong with you?" he'd ask.

Of course, I didn't have a good answer, and the sad expression on my face further annoyed him. Sometimes, we returned home to change my clothes, but this time, he made me ride the train in my wet garments to teach me a damp lesson.

Chapter 10

UNCONVENTIONAL

Twice a month on Fridays, my father's friends came over to play Poker or Gin Rummy. They drank a lot of alcohol and smoked weed until the wee hours of the morning. I always knew my place and would not enter the living room once the door had been closed.

My father's drug of choice was hash, and I knew it was something bad. He stored his little black block in a tobacco tin and went to extreme lengths to hide it. Sometimes, he put the small container in his dresser draw or at the back of the wardrobe he shared with my mother. He mistakenly assumed that I was oblivious to the shady activity going on around me.

Many nights, he donned an African robe, rolled a joint, turned the gram on, and played records by his favorite artists, James Brown, Otis Redding, and Percy Sledge. On occasion, he would say, "Analia, come here sweetheart. Sing daddy's favorite song fuh him."

From our record player, we heard James Brown's distinct voice belt out the lyrics to "Say it Loud – I'm Black and I'm

Proud." As requested, I sang along with James as loud as I could. My performance made my father crack up with laughter. Between his high and my singing, he was in hash heaven.

One night, I don't know what got into me, but I overstepped my boundaries and did something that made the monster in my father come out. My favorite game show called Opportunity Knocks aired on Friday evenings. On this occasion, Dad told me that he wanted to watch something else on a different channel. His program was going to come on at the same time as mine.

"Why can't I watch my show?" I asked.

"Because ah goin' ta watch football," he responded.

"Well, if you don't let me watch Opportunity Knocks, I'm going to tell the police what you have in that tin!" I yelled.

My father gave me a look that I had never seen before. He bolted over to where I stood and grabbed me by my shoulders. With his finger pointing in my face, he said, "Doh evah lemme hear yuh say nutin' like dat again! Try meh an' ah go cut yuh lil' tail! Yuh hear meh?"

While he yelled at me, I kept my head bent down and refused to make eye contact. He stuck his hand under my chin and jerked my head up to look at him. "Yuh hear meh?"

I started crying. "What de hell yuh cryin' for? Yuh want something ta cry for?" he asked.

"No Daddy," I answered.

"Well, shut up then!" he ordered.

My dad stormed out of the living room. I didn't see him again until the following morning. During our exchange, my mother sat at the dining table going over some bills and didn't say a word. Upon my father's departure, she told me I needed to mind how I spoke to him and that I should stop being rude.

Fortunately, she didn't give me a beating on his behalf.

***

Although my parents were strict, they didn't censor what I could read or watch on television. This was evident from my first exposure to *Playboy* magazine. A family friend of ours, whom I called Uncle Wilmot, stopped by after work one evening. As usual, he had the evening edition of the Sun newspaper with him.

Since I loved reading, I usually browsed through the papers and other magazines that my parents or friends bought. I didn't always understand what I read but could break words down into syllables and eventually pronounced them correctly.

My mother extended an invitation to Uncle Wilmot to stay for dinner, which he gladly accepted. He entered our living room, took his coat off, and laid his magazine on one of our coffee tables. From where I sat at the dining table, I could see the magazine's cover, with a picture of a white woman, with her breasts exposed. My curiosity was aroused. I had to get that magazine so I could look through it.

After dinner, my mom, dad, and Uncle Wilmot left the dining table and went to sit on the sofa to watch television. While the adults were engrossed in their program, I slowly inched my way to where Uncle Wilmot placed the magazine. Eventually, I just picked it up off the table and went back to my seat with it in my hands.

A few minutes later, my mother realized what I had done.

"Analia! What de hell is wrong with you? Go an' put dat magazine back now!" she yelled.

My father stopped talking to Wilmot and said, "Veronica, leave her alone. Let her look at it."

39

Veronica looked at him as though he were crazy.

"What kind ah stupidness is dat? How yuh goin' ta let a lil' chile look at a Playboy magazine, Victor?" she asked him.

In a calm voice, my dad said, "Aw gawsh. Let her see, so her curiosity will be satisfied nuh."

My mother shook her head and went into the kitchen. I went back to looking at those unforgettable pictures in Uncle Wilmot's "dirty book." I flipped through the pages and couldn't believe all the breasts and near-naked women I saw. When I got to the last page, I returned to the first one again. My dad stopped me and said, "Uh, uh. Gimme dat magazine. Yuh only get ta look at it once!"

***

Although I had many friends my age, I spent most of my time with adults. I was an only child for six years, and when my cousins and friends weren't around, I stayed close to my parents and theirs. My mother didn't mind me being in the same room with her and my father's peers, provided I stayed in my place. If they were conversing with another adult, I better not butt in or appear to be listening. I could not sit between two grown-ups, and I most certainly wasn't allowed to ask any questions.

To hear about the comings and goings of those in their inner circle, I kept quiet, played with my dolls or some other toy. I knew who was cheating on whom, how many women our upstairs neighbor, Bruce, had been with, and which one of my father's friends had been jailed for not paying child support or for possession of hash. If I sat there pretending to mind my own business, I got the scoop on many grown-ups. I also had to make sure that I didn't repeat anything I heard. Otherwise, there would be hell to pay with my mother.

I slipped up one time, but miraculously, I didn't get into trouble with my parents. Sheila, one of Bruce's girlfriends, came to our flat one evening. She assumed he wasn't home and asked my mother if she could wait for him with us until he returned. Little did Bruce's "girlfriend" know that he was upstairs in his flat with another woman.

While Sheila sat on our living room couch, I went to join her. She asked me those common questions adults tend to ask young children. Had I been a good girl, did I like school, what was my teacher's name, and what were my favorite toys? I answered her, then out of the blue, I blurted, "Yes, I'm being a good little girl, but Uncle Bruce is not a good boy."

"Analia, you're so funny. Why do you think Uncle Bruce isn't a good boy?" she asked me.

I giggled and said conspiratorially, "Because he's upstairs hiding from you." My mother, who had just returned to the living room, caught the last part of my disclosure.

She didn't know what to say or do and gave me a look that said, "Wait until your father gets home."

Sheila left our flat and stormed upstairs to where Bruce lived. A heated argument ensued, and we heard a lot of screaming and cursing from the floor above us. I was shocked when Mum started laughing and said, "Yuh see de trouble yuh 'cause?"

When my dad came home from work, she told him what I had done, which he found hilarious. I heard him tell my mother, "Good fuh he backside. Ah sick of his women always showin' up here lookin' fuh him. Dat is one less fool we go have ta' deal wid."

***

My parents often threw house parties, and during their fetes, I

41

was allowed to stay up with the adults. I did not like watching my dad dance with other women. If I thought they were dancing too close, I had no problem worming my way in between them with my arms folded across my chest. The look I gave dared them to continue. My dad found it comical that I had the nerve to tug on his pants leg and would laugh. I didn't find the situation funny, nor did I understand why my mother allowed him to crub up with her friends.

During one of their house parties, I witnessed my first case of physical abuse against a woman. The victim, a married woman, had been slow dancing with another man. Her husband, whom I'll refer to as "Mr. Boxer," did not like this blatant show of disrespect. He cursed his wife and the man that she was dancing with. From the tone of his voice and expression of anger, I could tell that something terrible was going to happen.

I scanned the room for my parents, but I couldn't find either one through the crowd of people that started to form around the "love trio."

Mr. Boxer attempted to grab his wife's arm, and when she pulled back, he landed a punch on her face that knocked her flat on her back, unconscious. Fear traveled through my little body. I had never seen anything like this before, and it frightened me.

My father, who had been in another room, finally emerged. Along with some of his other friends, he grabbed Mr. Boxer by his arms, collar, and other parts of his body that they got a hold of and threw him out the front door.

In the meantime, my mother and some of the other ladies attended to his wife. They passed a bottle of smelling salts back and forth under her nose, and shortly afterward, she came around. Many of the guests at the party wanted to call the police, but she begged them not to.

Chapter 11

LIKE MOTHER, LIKE DAUGHTER

V eronica...

Christmastime at our house was a wonderful time of the year. Most of the gifts under our beautifully decorated tree were for me. My mother, an excellent cook, and baker made white bread, sweet bread, and black cake. Everyone loved to come to our house to get some of her food.

Even though Veronica cooked traditional West-Indian fare like pigeon peas and rice, callaloo and crab, stew chicken, macaroni pie, and baked ham, I preferred my bland English food. I preferred my mashed potatoes, sausages, and baked beans.

During the holidays, my parents gave me a few sips of Baby Cham, which tasted just like Asti Spumante. Several times during our festivities, I tried to get more but was told, "Wait until you get older. Then you can drink as much as you want."

Barring several accidents, my early childhood was good. By the age of five, I had already been to France, received my first

Timex watch, and a fur coat with a matching purse. My parents also bought me a huge organ, which looked like a miniature piano. My dad insisted on me having it. I think he brought it so he and his friends could make "sweet music" as a prelude to their gambling sessions on Friday nights.

The wannabe musicians drove me crazy when they came over and latched on to my organ. I always had to tell my dad to make my uncles give me back my organ.

He'd chuckle and say, "Analia, doh be stingy. Let us play wid it for a lil' while longer, okay, sweetheart."

My mom would intervene. "Victor, why you an' those big horses monopolizing de chile organ? Give it back to her nuh. Goodness, who yuh buy it for?"

He didn't pay her any mind and conveniently ignored my look of frustration. The horses took forever to hand over my instrument.

My father encouraged me to share with everyone. Unfortunately for me, this included my playmates. When he took me to the park, I had to share my bike with friends who didn't have one. He explained that I needed to remember they were not as fortunate as me.

I didn't always agree with him. Some of these so-called playmates treated me like crap when they got in their funky moods. I was only allowed to pout for a minute or two, though, before I had to hand over my prized possession. Generous to a fault, Victor didn't tolerate selfishness.

Our family stood out wherever we went. My mother took pride in our appearance and made sure that we looked and smelled good.

When I attended birthday parties or had one of my own, Veronica straightened my hair and put a little makeup on my face. She loved Topaz, Occur, and Charisma, perfumes sold by Avon, and often sprayed one of those on me as well. I felt awkward, but that didn't matter. She even ignored my father, who told her that I was too young for all of that stuff. Veronica dressed and made me up as she saw fit.

Although my mother took great care of me, I longed for her to be more affectionate. My father demonstrated his love by giving me adoring looks, kisses, and warm hugs. He allowed me to sit up under him and always put his arm around my shoulders. Victor doted on me. Veronica did not. And in my child's mind, this equated to her not loving me.

We never developed a close mother-daughter bond. But I knew of her good qualities.

She worked hard, took care of her family, kept an immaculate household, and knew how to burn a pot.

My mother was loyal to her friends, but they did not always reciprocate. Folk that usually hung out at our house on Friday evenings, eating food and drinking with my parents, had a habit of speaking negatively about her out of jealousy. Once she discovered their backstabbing ways, my mother had no problem cussing them out and ending their friendship. Case in point. While at a party she decided not to attend, one of her girlfriend's, Maude, made some disparaging remarks about my mother to a mutual acquaintance.

"Jocelyn. Dat blasted Veronica is a little too much. She does go way over de top. Every time ah go to she house, she want ta put on a show fuh everybody. An ah nevah see a woman who could cuss like a sailor so. I doh know how a quiet man like Victor end up wid she," Maude stated. She mistakenly assumed that Jocelyn would not tell my mother about their conversation. She was wrong.

The next time Maude showed up at our flat, Veronica lit into her at the front door. I stood in the passageway and heard my mother say, "Here nuh yuh mudda ass. Doh come back to dis fuckin' house again. Yuh come in here, plant yuh ass on meh chair an' eat up meh food like a friggin leech. Den yuh have de nerve ta talk about I too over de top? Hole yuh ass. Victor know what it is he have an' he like it so. When yuh see me from now on jus', make sure yuh cross de street!"

Everyone always knew where they stood with Veronica as she was brutally honest. When a friend asked for her advice, they had better be prepared to receive it. She never told them what they wanted to hear; only what they needed to hear.

Teckler, another close friend of hers, was involved with a married man who treated her poorly. Whenever she came to our flat, she complained to my mother that he wasn't spending enough time with her.

"Veronica, when Boston come ta see me, ah does make sure ah cook what he want ta eat, an' a dere at he beck an' call. Ah taught he woulda leave he wife 'long time ago. What else he want from me?"

We were in the living room, where I sat on the floor by our coffee table, pretending to read one of my Janet and John books. But I was listening intently to their conversation.

"Teckler. You feel you is de only woman Boston have besides he wife? Girl stop being a blasted ass. Listen. Ah know you have feelins' fuh him, but when allyuh first meet, de man tell yuh he married. He ain't say a ting about leaving he wife. Is you who puttin' dat pressure on him now. Just leave him alone an' go an fine a man who doh have a woman or a wife. De same way yuh get Boston, is de same way yuh go lose him if yuh stay wid him.

Allyuh does do so, but yuh doh like so. I doh want ta see yuh get hurt."

Veronica was rough around the edges, but people gravitated towards her nonetheless. She was generous and a champion for her friends. And even though her delivery wasn't everyone's cup of tea, she showed her love the best way she knew how.

***

Clarinda...

It seemed as though the women in my family struggled with displaying affection. My maternal grandmother, Clarinda, was no exception. Granny was a strange woman. A typical vision of a grandmother is someone loving, affectionate, doting, and kind. Not mine. As with her daughter, I do not recall her hugging or kissing me. She limited her affection to the occasional obligatory, empty hug.

From a picture sitting on the mantelpiece in her living room, I knew that Granny had once been a gorgeous woman. But now, she barely resembled the light-skinned beauty with the warm smile in the photograph that I often stared at when I went to her flat. Stress from the toxic relationships she endured with my grandfather and other partners must have taken a toll on her.

Granny stood at five feet seven, had skinny legs, and walked like a gunslinger. She no longer pressed her curly hair and wore it in a shapeless afro, occasionally covered with a headscarf. Her light brown eyes were small, and she had thick eyebrows that were constantly knotted together. The dimples on both sides of Clarinda's cheeks were deep but only visible when she smiled, which was rare. My grandmother had a stern, intimidating countenance and always appeared to be angry.

Granny adored Orlando, her youngest child, and catered to his every whim. She allowed the brat to get away with things that I did not dare try with my parents. He had no manners, misbehaved all the time, and was downright selfish.

Visits to her house were bearable only because of her cooking. Her food wasn't spicy, and she made my English dishes just the way I liked them. Granny also did a good job combing my hair. My mother had a heavy hand which didn't bode well for me because I was tender-headed. Even though I had what people called "good hair," Veronica made it seem as though she were trying to comb through wool. When she brushed a section, I could feel her knuckles against my temples. If I tried to pull away from her, she would snatch me back by my hair. On the other hand, Granny took her time and gently passed the comb through my hair to avoid tearing through the tangles.

She lacked styling skills, but at least my plaits weren't too tight. I'm ashamed to say it, but those were the only two things I remember my grandmother doing nicely for me: cooking her bland English food and combing my hair.

Orlando and I fought a lot. Our mini brawls were always because of something he had done to irritate me. He never wanted to play with a toy, until I did. He never wanted anything to eat, until I did. If I accidentally nudged him while playing, he'd exaggerate, bring on the waterworks and tell my grandmother that I shoved him roughly. A tiny nick turned into the most painful cut ever. And he ate like a pig, smacking his lips and gobbling down whatever was on his plate.

Granny knew that her son was ill-mannered. So, to divert attention from his obnoxious behavior, she'd compare his offense of the moment to the time I tried to kill her when I was four years old. The attempt on her life took place one Sunday afternoon. My mother had invited her, Aunty Annette, Uncle Carl, and his family over for dinner. Granny and Veronica got into a dispute about something, and my grandmother started yelling at my mom. I picked up a fork, pointed it at Granny, and yelled, "Leave my Mummy alone!"

Everyone laughed at my actions. But not Clarinda. From that day forward, she did not like me. We both remained one another's least favorite people until well into my adulthood. It wasn't until years later that I found out why I had such a profound reaction to her. I learned the truth about how crazy she was.

Chapter 12

SIGNIFICANT CHANGES

O ne afternoon, I overheard a conversation between my
mother and Aunty Annette. I assumed they were making
plans for a party. However, they were talking about my parent's
wedding. My father promised Veronica that they'd get married
if they stayed together for five years after my birth.

My mother practically put the whole event together on
her own. She found a church for the ceremony and a venue
for the reception, made her wedding gown and dresses for her
bridal party, and baked and decorated her wedding cake. Aunty
Annette helped with a few tasks, but Veronica took care of the
important stuff for the most part.

On October 15, 1969, my parents were married at Saint
Paul's Episcopal Church in Ladbroke Grove, London. They had
a large wedding with a bridal party of seven bridesmaids, seven
groomsmen, three flower girls (one of them being me), and a
ring bearer.

When the wedding and reception ended, some of the guests

went to our flat for the after-party. All who attended had a great time. When I look at the one picture that I have of their wedding, I can say without a doubt that my parents were a beautiful couple.

On November 28, 1970, a significant event occurred in my life: the birth of my sister, Avianna. I had been an only child for six years and had no interest in sharing the attention I received with a sibling. Alas, my feelings were of no consequence. This baby appeared out of nowhere, and suddenly, the focus shifted from me to her. I was jealous!

My dad still showered me with his love. As for my mother, all the affection she failed to give to me went to Avianna. My little sister was the apple of her eye.

People said she looked like both of our parents, which made me resent her more. Resembling Aunty Annette was a good thing, but why couldn't I favor my mom and dad like Avianna?

I had to admit; my baby sister was adorable. Even Granny doted on her and often commented on her lovely, fair skin. Moreover, Avianna had an angelic face and big, beautiful light brown eyes, just like our mother. She was also a happy baby and hardly ever cried.

My father expressed to me the importance of understanding and fulfilling my role as a big sister.

"Analia, ah know yuh accustomed ta being an only child, but yuh have a sister now. Ah know yuh jealous of her, but don't be. Yuh still my baby an' ah will always love you. Nothing will change dat. So be nice ta yuh sister fuh daddy. Play with her gently, okay? Remember, she's still a baby," he coaxed.

***

Several months went by, and I still refused to embrace this big sister thing. Since Avianna's arrival, I felt displaced. I also felt as though I was losing the bond that dad and I had. His pep talk fell on deaf ears, and my spiteful streak emerged.

When the weather was nice, my mother would let me sit on a low wall outside our flat. Sometimes, Avianna stayed with me while sitting in her pram. Veronica always put the brakes on and told me not to take them off. If I did, I could lose control of the pram if it started to roll away.

For a few days, I thought about pushing Avianna's pram down the block to see what would happen. I was sure I could get away with a test run without any mishaps. And if I didn't, so what?

The day finally came when I put my plan into action. After sitting outside with Avianna for a few minutes, I kicked the brake lever up and started walking with her. Several times, I pushed the pram, let it go, then ran after it and caught it before it hit anything. I knew it was dangerous, but I didn't care. Besides, Avianna was having a ball, squealing, and giggling during our game.

My luck ran out. Eventually, I pushed the pram too far ahead of me, and this time, I couldn't grab the handle fast enough. At NASCAR breaking speed, the pram went flying down our street until it crashed into the letterbox at the end of our road. Who should turn the corner at the same time but my father?

"Analia! What yuh doing? Yuh crazy or what?" My dad ran over to the pram and picked up my screaming little sister. "Hush baby. Doh cry," he consoled her. "Analia, get de pram an' come on," he yelled at me.

He turned around and headed towards our house, leaving me to push the empty pram behind them. When we got inside, he told my mother what happened, and her first reaction was to beat me.

"Didn't ah tell yuh not ta mess with de lever? Why yuh so blasted hardened?" she asked loudly.

"Veronica, leave her alone. Ah already tell her off. It was a mistake."

She glared at me. "Mistake meh ass. Avianna could have been seriously hurt!"

My father shot back sternly. "Listen, ah said leave her alone. I'll talk ta her again a little later."

I felt awful for almost injuring my sister and began to cry. I went to my bedroom and stayed there until dinnertime. While my mother cleared the dishes, dad called me to where he was seated and told me to sit on his lap.

"Analia, yuh okay?" he asked. Still too upset to respond without crying, I shook my head instead.

"Ah sorry fuh shouting at yuh earlier, but Avianna could have been badly hurt. Dis is why we tell yuh not ta take de brakes off. Because of de lil' dip in de road, we knew yuh wouldn't be able ta catch de pram if yuh let it go. Ent dat is what happen? Dis is what me an' yuh mudda was tryin' ta avoid." His gentle tone made me start to cry all over again.

"What she cryin' for?" my mother asked.

"Veronica, ah talk ta her an' she understand what it is she do wrong. Analia darlin', doh worry about it. Daddy know yuh didn't mean ta hurt yuh sister." He gave me a hug and a kiss and reiterated his love for me.

Chapter 13

MAKING MOVES

S ometime in 1971, my mother made a decision that changed our lives forever. Her brother, Rendall, had been living in New York since the early '60s. Although blacks were fighting for their civil rights at that time, he believed more diversity existed in America than in England. Rendall constantly urged his sister to relocate to create a better life for herself and her family. Truth be told, Veronica had always been fascinated with the United States and dreamt of living in the same country as her favorite celebrities.

My father was a quiet, gentle, laidback soul. My mother was the total opposite: a go-getter, a risk-taker, the kind of woman who thought on a large scale. She had no intentions of living the rest of her life in London, where blacks were still treated like second-class citizens and were never allowed to forget where they came from. England was nice but too dull for an adventurous, progressive woman like Veronica Edmonds. Bigger and better things awaited her future.

My father had no desire to move to the States. He thought New York was too much of a "hotbed" and not conducive to raising children in a safe environment. He enjoyed living in London with his family friends, a stable job, and a slow pace of living.

Eventually, my mother won my father over and began making her move. She decided that it would be best to go to New York with Avianna and me, get a job, and then send my father to join us.

Before I knew it, our last night in our home on Harvest Road had arrived. On Saturday, September 12, 1971, a going-away party was thrown in our honor. We even had some pop stars in our midst, Mac and Katie Kissoon, a brother and sister duo, who provided the entertainment. My dad and his brothers knew them from when they hung out together in Port of Spain, Trinidad. The Kissoon's had released several singles that charted throughout Europe. I always felt special when they came to our flat to hang out. I'd share the news of their visits with my friends, but none believed that I knew them. They didn't realize until the evening of our party that I had been telling the truth all along.

At one point, someone asked Mac, who I knew as Uncle Gerald, to stop singing sappy love songs and suggested that he switch to something a lil' more upbeat. Guests became depressed after his renditions of "I'm Leaving on a Jet Plane, Whiter Shade of Pale and Sitting on the Dock of the Bay."

***

At around one o'clock in the morning, my dad called me to him and took me to my bedroom. We sat on my rolled-up carpet and with his arms wrapped around me, had our second-to-last conversation.

"Analia, tomorrow you'll be going on a plane wid yuh Mum an' yuh sister. Daddy isn't going ta see you fuh a while, but ah want yuh ta remember dat no matter where you are, I will always love yuh an' ah goh be thinking about you. Yuh have ta be a big girl an' help yuh Mummy take care of Avianna until ah see yuh again. Doh let anybody trouble you or yuh sister and mind yuh manners okay?"

As he spoke, I saw tears streaming down his face. I cried with him and asked why I had to go with my mother. I pleaded with him to let me stay.

"I don't want to leave you. I want to stay here. I don't like Mummy."

He shook his head in disagreement.

"Of course yuh like yuh mother. Yuh love her. Ah know she a little hard on you, but she loves you, too. Now be a good girl fuh daddy and doh talk about yuh mother like dat." I hugged him tightly and asked him to come over to be with us as soon as he could.

I woke up the next morning to a buzz of activity. My Aunty Annette bathed and dressed Avianna and me while my parents finished packing. Most of the people at our house the night before came back to accompany us to the airport. We all ate breakfast together then left for Heathrow Airport. After checking in, everyone waited around until it was time to board. My mother and father sat in one section while I sat with Avianna, our family, and friends in another.

Family members repeatedly told me to make sure that I behaved well for my mother as if I had a choice. They reminded me that I would have to help her take care of Avianna. My mother's best friend, Margaret, brought nine of her eleven children to the airport so they could also bid us farewell. During our wait, she stroked my face while telling me how much she would miss me.

Aunty Margaret and her children were like family, and I was close to them. I had a lot of fun at her house. There were always so many kids around, laughing, playing, and teasing each other. We had a few catfights, but for the most part, we got along extremely well.

Finally, it was time to board the plane. I kissed and hugged everyone goodbye and gave my mother some space to do the same. Then I walked over to where my father stood, observing the scene before him. Again, there were tears in his eyes, which made me start to cry. I just had to ask him one more time if I could stay with him. He picked me up, hugged me tightly, and said, "Analia, Daddy told you dat he will see you soon, right? Doh cry, sweetheart. Time is going ta fly by, an' I'll be wid you before yuh know it." He couldn't have been more wrong.

He put me down, and as I walked towards the gate, I looked behind and saw him kissing my mother and Avianna goodbye. Everyone watched as we went through the door that would lead us outside to the plane. From the waiting area window, I could see my father, family, and friends waving goodbye. I waved back, blew several kisses, and boarded the plane.

No one could have predicted the dismal future ahead of us. Almost a decade would pass before I spoke face to face with my father again. If only he had kept Avianna and me with him. If only he could see that he was about to lose the people he loved most.

My happy childhood was coming to an end.

Chapter 14

APPLE ANYONE?

O ur journey to America included a stop in Toronto, Canada. I didn't know this at the time, but we would enter the United States with doctored documents. We hoped to avoid an intense immigration inspection at either John F. Kennedy or LaGuardia Airports by driving across the border into New York.

We stayed with some of my mother's friends for a few days. Towards the end of our first week, Uncle Rendall arrived. He drove from New York in a 1971 gold Plymouth Duster. I found him to be much better looking than Uncle Errol. His huge Michael Jackson fro fascinated me. I also liked the simple outfit he wore; jeans with a navy blue shirt. None of the loud colors or geometric designs that his older brother wore.

As I continued to study Uncle Rendall, I noticed how much we resembled each other. He had a darker complexion than me, but at least he wasn't fair-skinned like my parents and sister. We had the same jet-black curly grade of hair and almond-shaped eyes. Even our lips were similar: thin and not full like most of my family members.

Uncle Rendall and my mother decided to spend an additional two days after his arrival in Canada before driving to New York. On the morning of our departure, we had breakfast with Monica and her husband, Dave. My mother and her girlfriend made plans to see each other again once we got settled. We said our goodbyes, and at 9:30 a.m., on September 21, 1971, we left and began our car ride to the Big Apple.

I sat in the back seat while my mother sat upfront with Avianna in her lap. Car seats hadn't been invented yet, and there weren't any seat belt laws in effect. It was customary to see an infant sitting in the passenger seat with an adult and nothing but that person's arms holding them in place. I caught my uncle looking at me through the rear-view mirror with a big smile on his face.

"Veronica, both of yuh daughters are beautiful, but there's something special about dat older one," I heard him say. He spoke with an American/Caribbean accent, like Uncle Errol.

My mother smiled and said, "She's a good girl. Ah can't say dat ah does have any problems wid her. But when she ready, Analia can be something else."

Uncle Rendall glanced at me and said, "Analia and I goh get along jus' fine." Then he asked, "Analia, yuh enjoy de plane ride? And yuh happy dat yuh visitin' a new place?"

I didn't answer right away. Although I had the pleasure of experiencing my first plane ride while traveling to the States, the novelty of it all didn't diminish the sadness I felt leaving my father behind. I missed him so much already. Finally, I said what I thought he and my mother wanted to hear. "Yes, I'm glad that I came."

He smiled again. "That's good. Yuh goin' ta make new friends, go to a new school and all of dat fun stuff, okay?"

I didn't want to make new friends or go to a new school. I was pretty happy with the friends I had in London, the school I attended, and most of all, my father.

I watched as numerous cars passed by. Soon, my eyes began to water. I tried my best to stay out of my uncle's view and kept my face pressed against the car window. I attempted to keep my tears at bay but to no avail. Eventually, they fell, and I continued to cry silently for quite some time before finally falling asleep.

**

We made a few stops to relieve ourselves, change Avianna's nappy, and eat. At some point, the road that we were driving on turned into three lanes with booths. The cars ahead of us came to a complete stop when they got next to their respective booths. Then, each driver handed something to someone inside. After a few minutes, they drove off.

As we neared our booth, I heard Uncle Rendall say to my mother, "If he asks yuh anyting jus' tell him dat we went ta visit a frien' in Toronto fuh a few days. Roll down yuh window." He looked over his shoulder and told me to do the same.

"Good afternoon. How is everyone doing today?" asked a man in a green uniform.

"Very well, thank you," Uncle Rendall replied.

"May I ask where you're coming from?"

"Sure. We were in Toronto for a few days, visiting with some friends." Uncle Rendall's Trinidadian accent was noticeably less pronounced.

The man nodded and said, "Okay. I need to see the registration for your vehicle and travel documents for all of your passengers."

Uncle Rendall handed over a piece of paper and several little blue books. The man in the uniform reviewed the document, then studied each of our faces as he opened the books.

"Okay, sir. You can proceed."

Approximately nine and a half hours after leaving Toronto, Canada, we arrived at our final destination, Brooklyn, New York.

During our brief stay in Canada, I saw a few places that reminded me of home. This was probably wishful thinking on my part. However, Brooklyn looked different from where I had lived in London. The roads were wide and had large cars parked on either side of them. Although traffic flowed steadily, many pedestrians darted from spaces between stationary vehicles to cross the street. There were tall structures and various businesses packed next to each other, with numerous patrons entering and leaving. Everyone walked fast as if they had somewhere important to be. But what stood out the most was the number of people I saw with the same complexion like mine. They were – *everywhere.*

Don't get me wrong; black people were not a novelty to me. Many West-Indians lived in London after immigrating during the late forties as members of the Windrush generation. The Empire Windrush was the ship that brought one of the first groups of immigrants from the Caribbean to the United Kingdom. But the number of blacks that I encountered could not compare to what I saw upon my arrival in this bustling city.

Uncle Rendall parked on Foster Avenue. We got out of his car and followed him as he walked through the courtyard of Vanderveer Projects. I looked up in awe at grey buildings that were six stories high. I had never seen so many flats in one place. Short poles with chain links between them cordoned off sections of grass as if to preserve designated spots. A few wrappers and empty bottles were strewn about, which I found strange. Even I knew better than to throw rubbish on the ground.

My uncle opened the door of building 3103 and led us to apartment 1F, located on the first floor. What would soon be his former flat impressed me. It was spotless. The living room furniture consisted of a three-piece, brown sofa set, smoked glass coffee tables, and a large television on a mini entertainment center against one of the walls.

All the kitchen appliances were brand new and gleaming white. The toilet and bathtub were in the same room, unlike our house in London. Those amenities were separate. There was a large bedroom in the back, where my mother, Avianna, and I would sleep.

I stayed in the living room with Avianna while the adults retrieved our suitcases from the car. When they returned from their final trip, another person entered the apartment with them. A small-framed, brown-skinned woman who looked like a young girl entered the room. She seemed to be as unhappy as I was. As she placed her handbag on one of the coffee tables, Uncle Rendall introduced us.

"Analia, this is my wife, your Aunty Clarissa. Say hello."

"Hello," I said.

We didn't exchange any smiles, and when she replied to my greeting, I could barely hear her. Honestly speaking, I didn't care. Uncle Rendall turned on the television and left his wife and me in the living room. We sat next to each other on the loveseat but did not speak. I had more social skills than Clarissa. *Wow! I thought to myself. If I responded as she did to a greeting, Mummy would be angry.*

I remembered the first time I mumbled "hello" to one of my adopted aunts. Veronica quickly ordered me to "Speak up! Yuh Aunty Merle can't hear yuh if yuh doh open yuh mout'." The second time I mumbled a reply to a question another adult had asked me, she said, "Analia! Ent ah tell yuh to speak up when somebody talkin' ta yuh? Ah doh want ta hear no mumblin'. Open yuh mout' an' talk."

My mother didn't have to tell me a third time to speak clearly when spoken to. From that moment on, I gave the biggest greetings and spoke loud enough to be heard. And if anyone made the mistake of asking me about how things were going at school or what were my favorite shows to watch on the telly, I'd talk their heads off. I was a chatterbox and often in my element when having conversations with adults and children alike. Clarissa was different. She looked uncomfortable, and I felt sorry for her.

In the meantime, my mother and her brother retreated to the kitchen to catch up on all that had been going on in their lives. More than twelve years had passed since they last saw each other.

***

I don't remember when Uncle Rendall and Clarissa left or when we got into our bed. However, when I woke up the next morning, Avianna sat in the middle, between my mother and me, sucking on her dummy. I heard the front door open and then a knock on the bedroom door.

"Wake up sleepy heads! Is time ta hit de streets!" Uncle Rendall excitedly proclaimed. "Analia, come on. Get dressed. We're going to meet some friends of mine."

I got out of bed, and he led me to the bathroom, where he showed me how to operate the shower. This was the first time that I had ever used one. In England, we only had bathtubs. My mother came into the bathroom to check on me and ensure that I wasn't splashing water all over the floor. After taking my shower, I got dressed in the outfit she took out and had my hair combed.

I was so excited about my pending outing with Uncle Rendall that I didn't want breakfast. I lied and told my mother that I was not hungry. She made me eat a slice of toast anyway. As soon as I ate the last piece, I stood up and placed my saucer in the kitchen sink.

"Come on Analia. Let's make some moves." Uncle Rendall didn't have to tell me twice. He took my hand, and as we reached the front door, he turned around and jokingly said to his sister, "Veronica, ah going ta cut Analia's hair so she can wear it in an afro. She have just de right type of face fuh one."

My mother cut her eyes at her brother and said, "Look, catch yuhself. Doh start dat Afro shit already. We jus' get here. An' besides, she too young ta wear her hair like dat. You make sure dat when yuh bring meh chile back, she looks jus' how she lookin' right now."

"Alright, alright, I was just kidding. Take it easy," my uncle replied as we exited the apartment.

Uncle Rendall might have been joking with my mother, but she was dead serious. Due to a bad experience that she had when she was fourteen, Veronica did not allow random people to comb my hair, although with her heavy hands, I sure wish she did.

She had some drama with a few older girls who went to her school. You know how females are. From a young age, we find fault with each other because one may wear nice clothes, is popular, smart, or pretty. You name it, and we'll find a reason. In my mother's case, she was disliked for being cute and having long wavy hair.

One day on her way home from school, her haters decided to jump her. They cornered my mother in an alley, and while three of them pinned her to the ground, the leader of the pack cut off one of her plaits. Even though she could hold her own in a fight, they got over on her because she was outnumbered. But they forgot that Veronica had two very protective brothers. The next day, each of the girls involved in the incident got double ass whippings; one from my mother and a combined one from Uncle Errol and Uncle Lloyd.

Chapter 15

THE HAREM

S hortly after our departure, we arrived at the apartment of
a lady named Sandra. She greeted me warmly as if we had
known each other for much longer than a minute. And the kisses
she gave to Uncle Rendall spoke volumes.

Sandra was short, dark-skinned, and very shapely. Her flat
stomach and wide hips were noticeable in the midriff top and
high-waisted Joyces she wore. Her hair had been parted down
the middle in two curly afro puffs and held in place with thin red
ribbons. She had a wide gap between her two front teeth, but it
didn't make her any less attractive.

I sat on the sofa, trying to make sense of what I had seen. Just
the day before, I met Uncle Rendall's wife. I had enough smarts
to know that when two people were married, they were not
supposed to be messing around with anyone else. The woman
at my parents' party came to mind. I recalled how her husband
punched her face for dancing with another man. Clarissa would
not be able to knock Uncle Rendall to the floor. But she wouldn't

be happy if she saw the way this friend of his had been all over him.

About a half-hour later, my uncle told Sandra he had some other stops to make but planned to return later that evening. I got up from the sofa and walked with them to the door. Sandra attempted to whisper; however, I heard her say, "Make sure you come back tonight. You're always running in and out. Stay this time."

Uncle Rendall patted her behind and kissed her cheek. She turned around to hug me goodbye and said she hoped I'd come back to visit her again.

Once we got in his car, Uncle Rendall looked at me with a sly grin on his face and said, "Analia, we're going ta see another frien' of mine. If she asks you anything about where we've been, jus' tell her dat we were driving around. Doh mention anyting about seeing Sandra, okay?" My confusion increased, but I nodded in the affirmative to indicate that I'd keep my lips sealed about Sandra.

Next, we went to Regina's apartment. She timed our arrival perfectly and opened her door before Uncle Rendall had a chance to ring the bell. Regina seemed just as nice as Sandra but quite different in appearance. She was tall, chubby, and light-skinned. Her large brown eyes were beautiful, round, and lined in black, giving her an exotic look. I liked her ponytail with ringlets that fell on the sides of her full, dimpled cheeks.

Uncle Rendall was more intimate with Regina. They pecked each other several times on their lips and swayed left to right while enjoying a long embrace. For a minute, I thought I had been forgotten.

They broke apart, and Regina turned towards me and bent down to get to my level.

"Hi, Analia. How are you doing, sweetheart?" she asked with a smile.

"I'm good thank you."

"I baked a cake for you. Would you like a piece?" Veronica would have had a fit if she knew that I ate cake without having a proper breakfast. But she wasn't around, so I accepted the offer.

"Regina, she hasn't eaten breakfast yet. Fix her something ta eat, and she can have de cake afterward." Uncle Rendall gave my head a playful nudge as if to say, "I know that you know better than to think you can have cake this early in the morning." He should have given that nudge to Regina.

My first American breakfast was delicious. I had little flat cakes with something sweet poured on top of them, bacon and eggs. I ate everything on my plate and drank two glasses of orange juice. You would have thought I had not eaten in days.

While my Uncle Rendall and Regina stayed in the kitchen to have a chat, I went into the living room to watch T.V. "Casper, The Friendly Ghost" was on. It quickly became one of my favorite cartoons.

Regina appeared and handed me a saucer with a slice of yellow cake covered in chocolate frosting. I decided that I liked her more than Sandra. She won me over with the delicious food that she fed me.

An hour later, we were leaving. Regina gave me a to-go bag with more cake. She kissed my cheek and said, "It was nice meeting you, Analia. You gotta make sure you come to visit me again." Adults say the funniest things to kids. How could I make sure that I would see her again? Was I going to drive myself from our place to hers?

***

We left Regina's apartment and went to a supermarket called A & P. I had never seen a grocery store this huge before. As we walked up and down the aisles, Uncle Rendall pulled various items off the shelves and placed them in our shopping cart. When we got to the cereal section, he told me to choose whatever I wanted and that I could get some other snacks as well. By the time we left, we had enough food that would last forever.

Before returning home, we made one more stop at another friend's house, the third woman in one day. Marlene Claire appeared mixed with Chinese or some other Asian ethnicity with her slanted eyes and porcelain skin. She had a small, oval-shaped face with delicate features and a tiny frame.

Marlene looked like the type of woman who didn't take any mess. She answered the door, and even though she smiled at me and said "Hello," she barely acknowledged Uncle Rendall. Her cool demeanor made me wary.

"Analia, it is very nice ta meet you. 'Ow yuh doin'?" she asked. Same comment, same question, different woman. Her accent was like our Jamaican neighbor back in England, Ms. Bogle. I learned later that Marlene's family did, in fact, hail from there.

We did not stay long at her house, which was fine with me. I had no clue why Uncle Rendall even bothered to visit Marlene. She lived with her parents, who didn't seem pleased to see us. They didn't say one word and vacated the living room just as we entered.

On our way home, I thought about Uncle Rendall and his friends. He reminded me of Bruce back in London. They both messed around with a lot of different women.

When we returned to our apartment, we unloaded the groceries from the car. My mother was surprised at the amount of food her brother had bought.

"Rendall, who all a dis food for? An' why yuh buy so much cereal?" she asked.

"Veronica, de food is for you an' de kids. Analia chose de cereal she wanted, which is fine wid me," he replied.

"Analia doh know what she wants," she scoffed. "She get yuh ta buy tree different boxes because yuh give her a choice."

"You feel I studyin' you? Is my money dat ah spend, so you shouldn't have a problem wid dat," Uncle Rendall replied with a smirk.

My mother smiled slightly and sucked her teeth.

"Oh Okay. Well, ah guess dize dat. Carry on wid yuh stupidness if yuh want."

Chapter 16

VANDERVEER

A few days later, Uncle Rendall and my mother encouraged me to go outside.

"Go an' make some friends with de kids in de front of de buildin'. Yuh can't stay lock up in de apartment all de time," Uncle Rendall said light-heartedly.

I felt awkward because family and friends had always surrounded me. Introducing myself to strangers was something new and unsettling for me. I didn't want to make Veronica angry, so I did as Uncle Rendall suggested.

I stood on the step leading to the door of our building and watched some girls as they jumped rope. After standing in the same spot for a while, one of them looked at me and said, "Hey, you just moved in or something?" She spoke fast, and I could barely understand her.

"Yes," I hesitantly replied.

"You know how to jump rope?" I nodded my head in the affirmative.

"You wanna join us?" Again, I nodded my head.

On that day, I became a member of the Matthews circle. The Matthews sisters -Vida, Donna, and Deedee were a peculiar bunch. I had a lot of fun with them, but at times, they could be bullies. They were popular and had clout around the projects because of their older brother, Willie, the neighborhood thug.

Even though they took me in as a friend, the Matthews often teased me about my weird name and funny accent. To them, almost everything about me was funny. While living in London, I never thought of my name as being that different. In time, I began to dislike the sound of Analia as well as Avianna.

Over the next few weeks, I went through an initiation process as the new girl in the "hood." When Vida and her siblings weren't around, the other kids in the project saw that as an opportunity to make me pay for the indiscretions of the Matthews clan. On several occasions, they punched me in the back, pulled my hair, or knocked me to the ground for no reason other than my association with the folk who lived in apartment 6F in building 3103.

One day, I tried to get my mother to have a serious talk with my attackers. I had just been picked on and went home to tell her about my woes.

"Did you hit the person back?" Veronica asked.

I took a deep breath. "No Mummy," I answered.

My mother ushered me into our living room, where she gave me the version of a self-defense course that she had learned from her brother as a child. But first, she issued a warning.

"Listen ta me. If yuh evah' come in here tellin' me dat yuh let someone hit you widout hitting dem back, ah go give yuh some licks. Ah didn't make you so yuh could be someone's punching bag, yuh hear meh? Yuh have ta learn ta fight back."

I couldn't believe she said that to me. When we lived in London, both of my parents would fight my own battles. Now she was threatening to beat me if I didn't retaliate against my bullies. Me being much smaller than some of my antagonists was of no concern to her. Veronica felt that I needed to stand up to them and not show any sign of weakness.

"When someone hit yuh, I want yuh ta do dis." She pulled me close to her and tapped me under my chin so that my bottom teeth hit the top row. It didn't hurt much. But with a little more force, a lot of damage could have been done.

Next, she lightly jabbed me in the throat and said, "Dis is another place yuh need ta hit someone yuh goin' an' fight. Come. Practice wid me."

Even with permission, I hesitated to lay hands on my mother. Under any other circumstance, I would never dream of hitting her. But she assured me that it was all right to hit her as hard as I could, so I did.

When I finally let go of an upper hook, Veronica shouted, "Good! Yuh have ta hit dem hard enough so dat dey know not ta mess wid yuh. All yuh need ta do is fix one of dem, an' you'll see. Dey goh tink twice about troublin' yuh again." I started smiling because I pleased her, and at the same time, I learned how to defend myself. I couldn't wait for the next person to try me without just cause.

***

With Uncle Rendall's help, my mother enrolled me in Public School 269, located right around the corner from where we lived. I made other friends to the dismay of the Matthews sisters, who were slightly jealous of all the attention I received because of my accent. Sometimes, during our lunch break, a crowd would gather around me and ask me to say words like glass, water, can't, and stop, etc. They were curious about how words were pronounced in England instead of the American way of saying them.

My teachers also liked me. I was well behaved and polite. When they asked for volunteers to read passages from our textbooks, I was usually the first to raise my hand. I breezed through the sections and had no difficulty pronouncing words that usually stumped my classmates. At the end of my reading, they'd nod their heads in appreciation with smiles on their faces.

Back home, I was an avid reader and fortunate to have parents who worked with me to develop my reading skills. They encouraged me to read the Janet and John books given to students at school as well as newspapers and magazines. My father would have me read out loud to him, and the excitement he showed when I "broke a big word down," as he used to say, made me feel like the most intelligent girl in the world. And since I always wanted to impress my dad, I practiced reading every chance I got. Despite my growing popularity, the bullying continued.

One day, while eating lunch, a girl named Sharon let out a loud, disgusting burp. When I looked over at her, she threw a cup of water in my face. This girl was almost as big as my mother. Once I recovered from the shock of what she had done, I charged towards her and punched her in her face. I just happened to connect with her nose, which caused blood to flow all over her clothes. She began to cry, which surprised me. I felt victorious. Sharon may have started the fight, but I ended it!

I heard the other kids in the crowd saying, "Ooh, Analia beat Sharon up! Ooh, y'all see that punch?" After demonstrating my knockout skills, I experienced a lot less bullying.

Another experience I had that I'll never forget took place

when I wore Skip sneakers to school, instead of Pro-Keds or Converse, which were the designer kicks back then. They may have lived in homes with worn-out furniture, old appliances, and linoleum on the floor that had seen better days, but somehow, the kids in the projects managed to dress in the latest fashion. You'd swear they came from money when in reality, their parents were barely making ends meet.

I needed a pair of sneakers for gym, so my mother asked Clarissa to take us shopping. We went to A & S (Abraham and Strauss), a department store located in downtown Brooklyn. I didn't know anything about name-brand items when I lived in London. So, when I selected my footwear, I chose a pair of sneakers that looked like the ones I owned back home, called Plimsolls. They were white, bright, and could not be missed.

When I wore them the Monday after our shopping spree, it seemed as though everyone in the entire school stopped to stare at my feet. Before the end of the morning, I learned I had made a big mistake with my shoe selection. They were so far down on the designer pole; even the kids on welfare would rather put on a pair of raggedy, designer sneakers than wear a pair of Skips.

During our lunch period, a few of my so-called friends gathered in a circle around me and stomped on my feet while singing a ridiculous song; "Rejects! They make your feet feel fine. Rejects! They cost a dollar ninety-nine. Rejects! Oh Rejects!" They kept repeating that dumb ass jingle until the lunch period was over.

I was embarrassed, but they were right. Pro-Keds, the designer brand sneakers, cost thirteen dollars, while my Skips were less than five. I never wore them to school again. When my mother found out the reason why, she did not force the issue. Instead, she said, "I can't afford ta buy any sneakers fuh twelve dollars right now. But as soon as ah get some extra money, I'll buy you a pair."

How did I go from being one of the best-dressed kids in my old neighborhood to being teased relentlessly because of the shoes I wore? I wanted to go back home and waited eagerly for the day my father would show up to rescue me.

Chapter 17

MARY

Uncle Rendall worked at the New York State Department of Labor. He pulled some strings to get my mother a job there also. Mary Matthews, Vida's mother, agreed to watch Avianna during the day, which worked out perfectly for Mum. When I got out of school, I went to the Matthews' apartment and stayed there with my sister until she arrived home from work. There were times when this arrangement was not to my advantage, especially when the sisters decided to give me the cold shoulder.

Mary Matthews was a nice lady but a little on the "slow side." She walked around with a lump of snuff stuffed in her chin and smelled like wine. My mother hadn't figured out that she was a functional alcoholic. She also didn't know about Mary's husband, Henry the tyrant, who often had his wife on pins and needles.

Henry worked for the Sanitation Department. I never saw him in any clothes other than his dark green uniform with his name blazoned across the pocket of his shirt. He was an intimidating man. My father had always been soft-spoken, loving, and affectionate. Henry was a mean son of a bitch!

When he came from work, he sat in his favorite chair with his smelly feet propped up on a worn-out ottoman and barked endless commands to his wife.

"Mary! Git in dat kitchen and git me a drink!" or "Git my slippers!" or "Put the TV on channel 7." Mind you, the chair he sat on was right in front of their television.

Henry and Mary relocated from South Carolina to New York in their teens. They weren't much older than my parents but looked as though they had seen some hard times. Mary appeared to be in worse shape than her husband. I saw weariness and desperation in her eyes. Henry disrespected her, and so did their children, who followed the example he set. I felt bad for Mary. She was the epitome of a woman whose spirit had been crushed. The kind of woman I had no familiarity with.

Her cooking skills were the only thing that she could be proud of. Whenever we entered the Matthews apartment, delectable aromas teased our senses. Her fried chicken, pork chops, and whiting were mouthwatering. She also made sponge cakes from scratch with vanilla or chocolate frosting that were scrumptious. I could not get enough of them. I enjoyed all of her food except for one dish – chitlins. No matter how much she tried to get me to taste that foul-smelling southern delicacy, I never caved in.

***

Mary's babysitting gig for our family ended about three months after it started. One afternoon, I saw Henry beat the shit out of her because his food wasn't hot enough. He punched her face several times before shoving her down on the sofa. I was terrified, but the rest of the Matthews clan seemed unfazed and kept their gaze glued to the T.V.

Later that evening, when my mother came to get Avianna and me, she noticed Mary's swollen, bloodied lips, the bump on her right temple, and a purple bruise under her right eye. We went home, and Veronica never let us return to their apartment.

I heard my mom tell Uncle Rendall and Clarissa about Henry assaulting Mary and the evidence she saw of her beating. She also made it clear that any man who put his hand on her or her children would suffer serious consequences.

"All I know is dat de bastard better not evah fall asleep because ah will kill him!" she exclaimed passionately.

Uncle Rendall laughed and said, "Veronica, you always ready ta fight somebody. Yuh tink yuh bad, eh?"

My mother rolled her eyes in response and said, "Yuh go see how bad I am if some fool try ta pull dat blasted shit on me or my daughters!"

Shortly after Mary's beating, Avianna and I started going to a babysitter in another building in our projects. Momma Jensen, as she liked to be called, lived in a lovely, clean apartment. The environment in her home was much more stable. Her children were well behaved, and she did not tolerate any nonsense from them, her husband, or anyone else for that matter. My mother loved her to death, and so did I.

I soon learned that Henry wasn't the only one who had a nasty temper. Surprisingly, Uncle Rendall had one as well. Clarissa was well into her pregnancy with their first child when I first encountered an ugly side of him.

***

She came to our apartment one evening after work. During her visit, she complained to my mother about her husband's infidelity. "Veronica, I hesitate to talk to you about your brother, but what Rendall is doing is wrong. He stays out late at night. Sometimes, he doesn't come home and acts as though I do not have a right to question him," she bemoaned.

Veronica looked at her and said, "He does it because yuh does put up wid dat nonsense. Why yuh still married ta him when he doesn't treat you right?" she pointedly asked Clarissa. "Bruddah or no bruddah, ah not stayin' wid no man who does be in de streets. But dat is your decision ta make, not mine."

A short time later, the doorbell rang. My mother peered through the peephole and saw Uncle Rendall standing outside. As she opened the door, I could hear him enter and ask harshly, "Where is Clarissa?"

Veronica knew that her brother was angry.

"She in de kitchen," my mother told him. "What is yuh problem an' why yuh so mad?" she asked.

Uncle Rendall didn't answer her. He stormed into the kitchen, walked over to Clarissa, and grabbed her by the neck of her maternity dress. He made her stand up as he pushed her against the kitchen wall. "Listen, if you ever destroy any of my tings again, I will tro' yuh ass out on de streets. Doh touch nuting' of mine without my permission as long as yuh live!"

Clarissa began to cry. That feeling I had when Mr. Boxer punched his wife resurfaced, and I got scared.

"Rendall, get yuh friggin' hands off of her! Yuh mad or what? Doh bring that shit in here!" my mother yelled at him.

"Veronica stay out of this!" he replied.

"Don't tell me no fuckeries 'bout staying out of nuting'! De woman pregnant an' you treatin' her so? Go somewhere an' cool off!"

Uncle Rendall released his hold on Clarissa and walked out

of the apartment. After he left, my mother asked what happened to make her brother so angry.

Clarissa sat back down at the kitchen table and stated that she had cut up a few of his clothes, cracked the screen on their new television, and did everything she could to destroy their telephone. She had gone off.

Veronica shook her head.

"Clarissa! Uh uh. Girl, yuh have ta be careful. You can't mash up de man tings like dat! Yuh know how particular Rendall is about his clothes, and you had de nerve ta cut dem up? You real brave," she stated.

Not long after that incident, Clarissa left my uncle and returned to her hometown in Little Rock, Arkansas.

Uncle Rendall had been unfaithful before and during their three-year marriage. It finally dawned on her that her husband would never change. He didn't marry her for love but as a pathway to get his citizenship. And while he may have told her otherwise, she had to have known that Rendall Walton was not marriage material.

Three months after returning home, Clarissa had a baby girl and named her Tiffany. Unfortunately, I never met my cousin. We spoke on the phone years later, but that was the extent of our contact. I don't know whether Uncle Rendall had anything to do with his daughter as he never spoke about her.

***

I often thought about my father: what he was doing and when he'd join us. When I asked my mother about him, she'd say, "He'll be here soon." I knew that she was trying to appease me, so I remained hopeful.

A deep void had been created by my dad's absence, which caused me to latch on to Uncle Rendall. Even though I hadn't forgotten about his fight with Clarissa, I pushed it to the back of my mind. He treated me nicely, and in my world, that is what mattered most.

Our relationship evolved into one like what I shared with my father in a short space of time. We went everywhere together. To visit his girlfriends, when he hung out with his male friends, who became my adopted uncles, to the basketball court across the street from our projects and food shopping. Every Thursday, he took me to Baskin Robbins to buy a cone with a double scoop of strawberry swirl ice cream and rainbow sprinkles.

I enjoyed the attention that Uncle Rendall lavished on me. However, there was a downside to spending so much time with him. I saw how he juggled relationships with several women, cheated on them, told lies, and used them to take care of whatever needs he had. His deception had no limits.

There were many occasions when he made plans to spend time with one female but ended up at the home of another. The day after his no-show, he would take me with him to the home of the woman that he should have visited. On the way, he prepped me on how to respond if any questions were asked concerning his whereabouts.

Some of his women were bold enough to question me in front of him. Others waited until he stepped out of the room to start their inquisition. Regardless, I always gave the response we agreed upon in advance.

Initially, I wasn't comfortable fibbing to his girlfriends, especially the ones that I liked. But my allegiance was to Uncle Rendall, and I would do my part to keep him out of trouble. So, with a sweet smile on my face, I continued to lie as instructed. And in no time at all, being deceptive came as easy as breathing.

Uncle Rendall didn't hide his love for the opposite sex. He stayed on the prowl, always looking for a new female to add to his stable. When we went out, we used the same scheme that always worked in his favor. After he spotted an attractive woman, he'd have me walk up to her and say, "Hello, Miss. That man over there, who is my uncle, wants your phone number." His prospects always found my actions cute. Predictably, they laughed in response and let me lead them to where he stood. Like a vulture closing in on its prey, he struck up a conversation, put his charm on full display, and walked away with a phone number.

Veronica knew about her brother's philandering, and that often used me as a pawn. But she took it all in jest. I continued to spend as much time with my uncle for as long as he allowed me to. I still missed my dad and wanted to be home in England. In the meantime, Uncle Rendall temporarily filled his shoes.

Chapter 18

ADJUSTMENTS

I adjusted to living in Brooklyn, despite the neighborhood bullies. I enjoyed school, loved the diverse children's programs on TV, songs I heard on the radio, and watching Don Cornelius' Soul Train, which aired on Saturdays at 11:00 am. I also liked the variety of foods and sweets. I got hooked on Strawberry and Grape Now and Laters, Swedish Fish, Charms Blow Pops, Bazooka Gum, Charleston Chews, and Apple and Watermelon Sticks. Uncle Rendall always gave me a quarter for pocket money, which I would spend on junk food at the neighborhood Five & Dime store. On those days, I lived in candy heaven.

The only black celebrities that I knew of in England appeared in a sitcom called the Desmonds. However, in the States, there were many more blacks on television. Finding out that Michael Jackson had a cartoon show shocked me. On Saturdays, I never failed to watch the Jackson Five cartoon show. Julia starring Diahann Carroll, and the Flip Wilson comedy show, also aired but were geared towards adults. Still, I was amazed to see this beautiful, black woman in the lead role of a television program. I also enjoyed the Brady Bunch and wondered what it was like to live in a spacious house with five siblings and a maid in a part of the country that was always sunny. On the opposite end of the spectrum, I tuned in to Creature Features, which came on right after Soul Train.

My mother let me watch TV until one o'clock on Saturdays. Then, I had to help her with house cleaning. At seven years old, she expected me to help take care of Avianna, keep the apartment tidy, and cook. Veronica wanted me to be independent and thought it essential for me to handle specific tasks at an early age.

While other kids didn't even know how to bathe themselves properly, I washed my baby sister, cleaned the bathroom, dusted furniture, and cooked side dishes like rice and vegetables. I knew how to mix Avianna's baby formula and did a good job of feeding her, too.

I didn't mind completing my chores as my mother rewarded me with extra pocket money when I did a good job. She was nice at times but still inadequately affectionate.

***

On most Saturdays, Uncle Rendall visited. He often had two brown paper bags filled with Candy, which he gave to Avianna and me upon his arrival. He knew I liked Apple Stix and made sure that he included one of the bars in my bag. This candy took forever to eat. First, because it was so hard, you couldn't bite it. Second, you were forced to take your time sucking it until the bar finally whittled down to a size where you could pop the remainder into your mouth.

I am not sure how Avianna managed to accomplish this impressive feat, but one day, she finished hers before I ate mine.

When she realized that I hadn't consumed my bar, she tried her hardest to take it out of my hand. I wasn't having any of it.

"Leave me alone Avianna! You're so greedy!" I shouted in frustration.

My mother appeared out of nowhere and asked, "What yuh jus' say ta her?"

Without thinking, I repeated what I said. "I told her to leave me alone and that she's greedy."

I guess Veronica didn't appreciate my tone of voice. Once the last word came out of my mouth, she slapped me hard across my face. "Listen ta me. Doh eva talk ta yuh sister like dat again! She's only a baby. Who yuh tink yuh callin' greedy? Give me dat blasted candy!" she yelled. Veronica grabbed the remainder of my Apple Stix from my outstretched hand, gave it to Avianna, and told me to go to our bedroom.

Uncle Rendall went to the park across the street to play basketball, so he missed my mother's outburst. When he returned and found me in the bedroom crying, he asked his sister what happened. After she got through telling him that I was selfish and always mistreating Avianna, he had a few choice words of his own for my mother.

"Veronica, yuh realize dat Analia is a child and right now, she probably feeling a little jealous of Avianna. You have ta admit it. Yuh does pay more attention to her than Analia. And why would you slap de child so hard? Jus' because she call Avianna greedy? Nah. Dat is a little extreme."

"Listen, doh tell meh how ta raise or discipline my children. These two only have each other, and ah want Analia ta learn dat from now! When dey get older, de only one who will be in her corner is her sister!"

After that incident, my mother tried to spend more time with me, and she let up a little on spanking me for *every* minor infraction. However, I didn't trust this new Veronica and remained distant from her. We never had a close relationship. It took some time for me to get accustomed to her sudden show of affection.

***

Veronica felt right at home, living in New York. She had always been a people person, and others enjoyed being around her. After becoming close friends with a few of her co-workers, they were invited to our apartment on several occasions. They played records, had a few drinks (even though she didn't indulge), ate dinner, and talked about the cultural differences between England and the States. When visiting, her friends brought treats for my sister and me. Everyone loved Veronica's daughters.

Uncle Rendall often came by with his girlfriend, and one evening, he showed up with his lady of the moment, Marlene. This one was from Trinidad.

Marlene Peterson was gorgeous, and she knew it. She had a chocolate complexion, high cheekbones, and a slim face. She wore her hair pulled back in a bun that sat perfectly on top of her head, making her look a few inches taller than her actual height of five feet, eight inches.

The first time Marlene came with Uncle Rendall to visit us, she wore a multi-colored shirt with bell sleeves, exposing just the right amount of her décolletage and bell-bottom Joyces. I could see why my uncle found her attractive.

Marlene and my mother clicked instantly. She became our adopted aunt. Mum and her new "running partner" did everything together. They went shopping for clothes, food, and furniture and accompanied each other to house parties. While they were out one night, my mother met the man who ultimately played a significant role in ending her life.

Chapter 19

MAMA'S NEW MAN

One Friday evening, Aunty Marlene came to our apartment with her brother, Alex. They were much closer to each other than the rest of their eleven siblings and often hung out together. Alex seemed nice. He was tall, good-looking, and dark-skinned, just like his sister. His tinted glasses were stylish, and the leisure suit he wore fitted him well. Without knowing they were related, one could see the strong resemblance between them.

As my mother introduced me to Alex, she never took her eyes off his face. The intense gaze they shared left no doubt in my mind that she had met him before. I did not want him anywhere near her.

"Analia, this is Alex, Aunty Marlene's brother. Say hello."

I said, "Hi," then asked if I could be excused. I retreated to our bedroom, leaving everyone outside, including Avianna. The adults had a conversation. I heard my mother laugh periodically. Since I didn't want to listen to her having a good time or hear

Alex's voice, for that matter, I turned the television on and raised the volume to a level where I could drown them out.

During dinner, I sat at the kitchen table, ate my food without saying a word, and again, left them to enjoy each other's company.

"Veronica, what's wrong wid Analia?" I heard Marlene ask my mother.

"Marlene doh pay her no mind. Analia in she own world," my mother responded.

"But yuh tink she alright?" Marlene asked again.

"As ah said, she in her own world. And she could be moody too yuh know. De best ting ta do is ta leave her alone."

"I ain't know nuh," Marlene replied. "A little girl like dat shouldn't be so withdrawn. Dat is not normal."

"Normal or not, dat is just how Analia is," Veronica stated.

It never dawned on my mother that I might be missing my father and going through changes because of our separation. We had been living in Brooklyn for over a year, and during that time, I had no communication with him. My mom expected me to go on with my life without my dad. Instead of taking the time to offer reassurance, her idea of dealing with my mood was to leave me alone.

Alex started coming over to visit regularly. His presence irked me. He appeared to be a little too comfortable with my mother. I could tell that something was going on between them. When they sat on the sofa in the living room watching television, he put his arm around her shoulder, or she'd rest her head on his. When he thought I wasn't looking, he'd pat or squeeze her butt, which made her laugh.

On numerous occasions, I went to bed, not knowing when he left. He had taken my father's place in my mother's life, and that pissed me off. To show my anger, I ignored his attempts to engage me in any conversation by barely responding to him; one-word answers, that's all he got. I stayed in our bedroom when Alex was around. If my mother dared to put Avianna in there with me, she became the object of my anger.

I made her cry by pulling her pacifier or bottle out of her mouth while drinking her formula. I knew that as soon as my mother heard Avianna crying, she'd come into the bedroom to discover the problem. I extensively used this ploy to get her away from Alex.

***

The light tapping on my face and of Avianna's cries woke me up. I assumed my mother hadn't heard her because she was still asleep. I raised my head to look over on her side of the bed, only to find it empty. The spot in which Veronica had lain in earlier had been replaced with pillows. I found Avianna's bottle under our blanket, courtesy of the moonlight illuminating our room.

I got out of bed, picked up my sister, and headed towards the kitchen to fix her a bottle of formula. I opened the bedroom door to see a pull-out cot in the middle of the floor with two bodies on it. I walked gingerly over to the cot and realized that my mother and Alex were asleep, dead to the world and naked as the day they were born.

I stared at them for a moment. Alex lay behind her, cupping her. Slowly, tears started to fall. At that moment, hatred for my mother and Alex was born. They were doing what my father tried to accomplish with my mother on many nights with me in their bed back in England. I knew that she should not be sleeping with this man, and as soon as I got the chance, I would tell my father what his wife had been doing.

I walked to the kitchen and put the kettle on to boil water for Avianna's formula. Once the water was ready, I prepared her bottle and returned to our bedroom. Through all the commotion I made in the kitchen, the lovebirds continued to sleep. They didn't even hear the kettle whistle.

I stayed up for quite some time after getting back into bed. All of my thoughts were about my father. I didn't know how I'd get his address, but somehow, I would find it. I had to write him a letter and give an update on everything that was going on. I needed my dad to take me to live with him. I did not want to remain in the same household with Veronica any longer.

Morning could not come fast enough so I could show my ass off to my mother. I planned to ask her outright why she and Alex went to bed without any clothes on. She had to know that I saw them. At this point, I didn't even care if she chose to beat me. Nothing could hurt me more than seeing her as I did earlier.

Before I could fall asleep, I heard the two lovebirds moving around and talking. Someone got up from the cot and entered the bathroom. I could tell that it was Alex because my mother's bracelets jingled while she folded the sheets and, eventually, the cot. A few minutes later, Alex got dressed, kissed my mother goodbye, and left.

After seeing him out, she returned to our bedroom, put on her nightgown, and got back in the bed. I never mustered up the courage to ask my mom anything about her and Alex. Instead, I distanced myself from them as much as possible and continued to wait for the day when my father would arrive.

Chapter 20

COUPLING

My mother and Alex let it be known that they were officially "seeing" each other. Uncle Rendall made it abundantly clear that he disapproved of their relationship. Veronica did not consider his opinion, nor the impression made on me.

There were many nights when I heard my mother and Alex making love. Since the night I discovered them naked, I stayed up to see when she'd sneak out of our bed to be with him. On several occasions, I couldn't keep my eyes open, but sure enough, the squeaking from the cot woke me up as well as my mother's cries of "Oh God, Alex! Oh God! Yes! Yes!"

I never heard her call my father's name like that. Perhaps me being in the middle of them stifled her expressions. Nevertheless, her newly found freedom and the passion they shared disgusted me. I also heard Alex moaning and calling my mother's name in a low, controlled voice while pumping away as if his life depended on it. I knew when they were almost finished. He'd push faster while they both started their symphony of moaning and groaning and all other kinds of noises that are made during sex.

While this went on, I sat in our bed and counted the number of times the cot squeaked until they finished. Then I listened to them kiss each other while trying to control their labored breathing. Eventually, they fell asleep, and only an occasional car passing by was heard in the quiet of the night.

Sometimes, I cried because I was so angry. I hurt for my father, who had shown nothing but love for me, my mother, and my baby sister. I hurt for him because I knew he was a good man and didn't deserve to be betrayed like this. I hurt because there wasn't anything I could do to stop what happened right before my eyes. He lost my mother to another man.

***

A few months into their relationship, Alex and Veronica threw a house party. A few of her girlfriends came over on the day of their fete to help set things up, cook the food, and whatever else needed to be done. While they were getting things ready, I kept Avianna occupied in the bedroom and watched her as she played with her toys.

Later that afternoon, my mother went to the store with her friends while I stayed at home with Avianna and Alex. Shortly after her departure, my sister fell asleep. I turned down the volume on the television and went into the kitchen to get a snack.

The sofa, loveseat, and armchairs were lined against the living room wall, and the coffee tables, placed in the kitchen. The television remained in its' usual spot. Alex sat on a folding chair in front of it. Out of the blue, he said, "Analia, come and watch television with me." He motioned for me to sit on his lap and said I could change the channel to whatever I wanted to watch.

I slowly walked over to him and, as suggested, sat on his lap. He pulled me closer and placed both of his arms around my waist to keep me from sliding off his lap. I felt awkward but remained in my position, as I didn't know what else to do.

Suddenly, Alex took one of my hands and placed it on a bump. He moved my hand back and forth over the bump, which felt soft at first. But slowly, it seemed to grow and harden. He covered my hand with his and pressed down on the bump. He slightly raised my hand then press down on it again. A rhythm began to form, and his breathing accelerated.

When I looked down to see what he was doing, he whispered, "Look at yuh show." I remember blankly staring at the television while he orchestrated my hand movements over his bump. The session he conducted continued for what seemed like forever. Finally, Alex told me to get up and go back into the bedroom if I wanted to. I left immediately, sat on our bed, and tried to make sense of what just occurred.

Something told me that what had taken place was wrong. I did not say anything to my mother or Uncle Rendall. I cannot explain my reason for not telling them. I guess I was too afraid of the outcome.

Years later, I realized that Alex made me rub his penis. He took advantage of me and used my little hands to give him pleasure. I often wondered whose side Veronica would have taken if I had mustered up the courage to tell her what he had done.

By the fall of 1972, I accepted that I wouldn't see my father anytime soon. I managed to find just a little bit of comfort, knowing that I still had Uncle Rendall in my corner.

My mother had given Alex a key to our apartment, and he often showed up before she returned home from work.

Occasionally, he tried to act like a father figure, but I paid no attention to him. If he told me I couldn't go outside to play after school, I went anyway. If he said I wasn't allowed to eat any snacks before dinner, as soon as he turned his back, I headed to the kitchen and ate whatever I wanted.

Initially, Alex didn't tell my mother about my disobedience, but he had to say something eventually, as I disrespected him every chance I got. Strangely enough, Veronica never disciplined me for acting up with her lover. She had a few stern conversations with me. However, no spankings were involved unless she felt I had gone way overboard with my rebellion. Little did I know that there was someone behind the scenes who attempted to help her see things from my perspective.

Chapter 21

MY FAVORITE TWIN

Lorraine Johnson worked with my mother at the Department of Labor. Initially, when passing each other in the hallway, they exchanged greetings but said little else. But after attending the same job luncheons and parties thrown by mutual co-workers, they formed a friendship. The two of them became close and, along with Aunty Marlene, spent a lot of time together.

I met Lorraine when she came to our apartment one evening after work. Ms. Johnson was a striking woman. One of the prettiest I had ever seen. She donned a curly afro, had a small, straight nose and thin lips. Her caramel complexion was flawless and contrasted sharply against her hazel-colored eyes. She had thick thighs, and a big ass that I was certain drew a lot of attention.

From the first day I met Ms. Lorraine, I knew she was someone special. I liked her warm smile and tight hug. She got a kick out of my accent and wanted to talk to me all the time. As I answered her questions about school and everything I could remember about London, she turned to my mother and said, "Veronica, I can't get over how smart Analia is. Your daughter is something else!"

Before long, Aunty Lorraine, as she became known to us, asked my mom if I could spend the weekend with her. She lived in the Marcy Houses (a/k/a Marcy Projects) in the Bedford Stuyvesant section with her mother and younger brother, Danny. The apartment they shared had been her home since birth. Aunty Lorraine also had two sisters, Diane, the eldest, and her identical twin, Loretta. They were married and lived with their families in Queens and Staten Island.

On my first visit to Aunty Lorraine's apartment, I met her mother, who insisted that I call her "Ma," just like her children and everyone else in the neighborhood. Lenora Johnson didn't resemble any of her children. She reminded me of my mixed-race cousins back in London. Jet black wavy hair parted in the middle fell just below her shoulders. She had fair skin, a round face with plump red cheeks, and a much wider nose than Aunty Lorraine. Her brown eyes were small and unremarkable, nothing like her daughters. Ma was overweight and moved around slowly, as though she had twenty-pound weights on her ankles.

During my time spent with Aunty Lorraine, we stayed around the projects. She introduced me to everyone as her goddaughter. I met several families with children close to or the same age as me, which was great. My new friends and I played outside until eight or nine o'clock at night.

Aunty Lorraine had one of the kitchen cupboards stocked with all the goodies I liked to eat, including Captain Crunch cereal, Chips Ahoy cookies, pickles, and Wise Onion & Garlic potato chips. Visits with her increased and became some of the happiest times I experienced while living in Brooklyn. There was always so much to do. We went to the movies, ice-skating, took trips to the circus and Bear Mountain State Park. Lorraine and her sisters were fun-loving people who adored children and enjoyed doing activities with them.

***

I became attached to my "godmother" and wanted to be with her all the time. I preferred to be with her even more than with my mother. I hated returning home on Sunday evenings. When the time came for me to leave, I couldn't disguise my sadness. Aunty Lorraine tried to make me feel better with words of encouragement.

"Don't be upset, Analia. I'll see what Mommy says about you coming over again soon, okay?"

Sure enough, no more than two weeks would pass by without me spending another weekend at her house. I spent most of my time with Uncle Rendall and his women or in the Marcy Projects with my newfound family. If I didn't have to be around my mother and Alex, I was happy as a lark.

During one of my visits, Aunty Lorraine sat me down to talk with her. She said my mother had expressed concerns about me and wanted to know if anything was on my mind.

"Analia, you know that you can talk to me about anything. If Veronica has done something wrong, tell me, and I'll speak to her for you."

I knew I could trust her, so I asked what I had wanted to know for quite some time.

"Why is she letting Alex spend so much time at our flat? And why isn't my father here yet?" Lorraine nodded to indicate she understood my question.

"Is that what's bothering you?" she asked, seemingly concerned.

I looked down at my hands and hesitantly answered, "Yes."

"Well, I can't say for sure why your father isn't here yet. Hopefully, he's still planning to come. As for your mother and Alex, all I can say is that they care about each other and want to spend as much time together as possible. I know it doesn't look right, but you have to respect your mother's wishes. Listen, sweetheart. I know this is hard for you, but as you get older, you'll understand."

I frowned. What she said made no sense to me. I wanted her to explain why my mother cozied up to another man besides my father. I wanted her to explain why she snuck out of our bedroom at night to sleep with him in our living room. And I would have appreciated her explaining why they made so much noise doing what they shouldn't be doing when they thought I was asleep!

No, it didn't matter what anyone said, including Aunty Lorraine. Veronica Edmonds was dead wrong for being involved with Alex and abandoning my father. I disliked them both, and my feelings would never change.

"Analia, I'll be here for you. If ever you need to talk, just pick up the phone and call me at home or work, baby. Everything is going to be okay. You'll see." She saw the skepticism on my face. However, to please her, I nodded in agreement.

My mother connected with Aunty Margaret's estranged husband, Patrick. Veronica's friends had been separated for years and had moved on with other partners. Patrick was involved with another woman, Cynthia, and they lived together in Brooklyn's East New York section. After being introduced to each other, Ms. Cynthia became a part of my mom's inner circle.

Patrick's lady adored Avianna and often took her to spend weekends at her house. My sister never returned home without a new outfit or toy. Just as Aunty Lorraine became my godmother, Ms. Cynthia became Avianna's.

Chapter 22

LAST THOUGHTS

We were close to Christmas of 1972, and I felt so excited. After all, this was my favorite time of the year. The balconies of the projects were decorated with lights along with the single-family homes in our neighborhood. At school, we drew pictures depicting the holiday season and hung them on the walls of our homeroom.

The Glee Club began rehearsals for our holiday concert, scheduled to take place on the day before we broke up for winter recess. But the most important thing on everyone's mind centered around the presents on their Christmas lists.

My mother's finances improved, and she saved enough money to purchase new furniture for our bedroom and living room that reflected her taste, not Uncle Rendall's. She also bought a floor model stereo with a built-in screen that looked like a television. When we pressed the appropriate button, the monitor lit up, and rainbow-colored lights went slowly around in circles.

As far as I knew, we were the only family in our building who had a system like this. Once again, my mother set us apart from everyone else. I loved playing our 45 rpm records on that stereo. We had all the latest songs - "I'll Be There" by the Jackson 5, "Oh Girl" by The Chi-Lites, and "Love Train" by The O'Jays.

A few days before Christmas, we finally decorated our tree. Everyone participated, including Alex. I passed the hooks for the ornaments to him and remained pleasant during our interactions. As much as I didn't care for him, even he couldn't spoil my good mood.

My mother brought out presents that she had been hiding and placed them under our artificial pine tree. I could barely contain my excitement when I saw the numerous gifts with my name on them. December twenty-fifth couldn't come fast enough.

One evening, the Matthews came downstairs to visit, and they were shocked to see the changes in our apartment. "Veronica, you done set yourself up nicely, huh?" Mary asked.

My mother smiled and said, "Mary, it was jus' a matter of time. Ah had it a little hard when ah first get here, but tings have gotten a little easier. Ah doin' much better now."

"Sounds good to me," Mary said with a chuckle. Although she seemed genuinely happy for us, her daughters did not. Vida, Donna, and DeeDee accused us of showing off and stopped speaking to me. I didn't care. I had more than enough playmates between the friends I made in school, plus the ones at the Marcy Projects.

***

On Christmas Eve morning, my mother began baking

sweetbread, white bread, and black cake. She also made traditional Caribbean holiday drinks like ginger beer, sorrel, and punch de crème.

Later in the day, she received a phone call from my Uncle Rendall. I overheard her telling him that one of Alex's sisters was having a Christmas Party. All of us, including Avianna and me, would attend. From what I gathered, Uncle Rendall voiced concern about inclement weather headed our way.

A mixture of sleet and freezing rain was expected to start falling at about nine o'clock that evening. According to the news, motorists were advised to stay off the roads. Still eavesdropping on her conversation, I heard her say to my uncle, "No, ah didn't hear anyting about de weather. Nah man. We accustom. Yuh worryin' too much about de snow."

They continued their conversation. My mother became agitated, and her facial expression soured. She placed her hands on her hips and assumed an angry posture.

"Aw gawsh, Rendall. Stop wid dat nuh! If ah want ta go out den dat is meh business!" She paused for a minute then said, "Okay. Ah will see yuh later." Veronica hung up the phone and returned to her baking. At seven o'clock, she called me into the kitchen.

"Analia, go an' put on de clothes ah leave on de bed. Yuh Uncle Donald is going ta take you to de party with Susan and Joanne while ah finish bakin'."

I wanted to scream! Donald wasn't my uncle. Why she insisted on referring to him as such baffled me. He was Alex's older brother, and I did not like him or his daughters.

" I don't want to go to that party, and I don't like Donald or his daughters," I whined.

"Well, if yuh doh want ta go, yuh could stay here by yuh blasted self!" she replied angrily.

At first, I didn't move. I just stood there for a minute thinking about how much I hated her. I said as much in my head before walking out of the kitchen. I changed my clothes, hoping against all odds that Donald would be a no-show.

Unfortunately, he arrived on time with Susan and Joanne. These girls were overweight, spoiled piglets who took pleasure in teasing or pinching me when adults weren't around. I detested being in their company and despised Veronica more for making me go to this family event with them.

"Analia! It's time ta go! Donald is here!" my mother called out to me.

I emerged from our bedroom as slowly as I could. When I reached the front door, Veronica handed me my coat. I stood in the doorway while I put it on along with my matching hat and gloves. I wrapped my scarf around my neck and left with the "Munster Family." I don't know how I got away with this, but I left without saying goodbye to my mother. I wish I hadn't.

Chapter 23

12.25.72

We arrived at Hazel's house at eight o'clock. Even though I was not fond of Alex or his awful nieces, I couldn't say anything negative about his family. His sisters treated Avianna and me nicely, whether my mother was around or not. That night, all the Peterson siblings were there, including the family matriarch, Ms. Junie. They went out of their way to make me feel welcomed while I waited for Mum and Alex to arrive.

Everyone had a great time drinking and dancing to calypso music. At ten-thirty, I walked into Hazel's kitchen to get a snack and heard Marlene ask her sister if my mother or Alex had called.

"No, ah ain't hear from dem as yet. Honestly speaking, ah taught dey woulda been here already. Yuh tink ah should call dem ta find out where they are?" Hazel asked. Aunty Marlene told her she should probably check on them.

Hazel dialed our number on her kitchen phone, and after a minute or so, she hung up. "Dey must be leave already. I ain't get no answer," she stated.

Aunty Marlene turned to me. "Analia. Yuh okay?" she asked.

"I'm fine. I just wish Mum would hurry up and get here. It's getting late," I told her.

"I know sweetheart. I'm sure she'll be here soon," she replied, attempting to sound reassuring.

The clock on Hazel's mantelpiece struck twelve. Christmas morning had arrived, and we hadn't seen or heard from my mother. I sat on the sofa in the living room, wondering what took her so long to arrive. At 1:00 am, Donald announced that he was going to leave.

"Listen, ah going ta make a move. It gettin' late an' it seem as though Veronica and Alex change dey mind. I'll take Analia an' drop her off at their apartment."

As I listened to him, I thought to myself that, knowing my mother and Alex, they had probably been "doing it again" and had fallen asleep. I was angry!

By the time we left Hazel's house, snow was falling heavily and sticking to the ground. If we got at least three inches, the projects would be swamped with snowball fights later than morning.

When we arrived at our apartment building, Donald came to the front door with me while the gruesome twosome remained in his car. I rang our doorbell several times, but no one answered.

"Well yuh mother an' Alex must be gone ta de party after all. Ah think you'll have ta spend de night by me an' ah will bring yuh home in de mornin'," Donald said.

"Can't we go back to Hazel's house so I can meet my mom?" I pleaded.

"No. It wouldn't make sense ta do dat. It already late an' besides, we're close ta my house. Wid dis heavy snow coming down, ah doh tink we should risk driving all de way across town ta Hazel's. Doh worry. Ah know tomorrow is Christmas. I'll make sure ah take you home early in de morning. Yuh will get ta open all yuh presents on time," he replied.

I didn't want to spend the night at Donald's house because this meant I'd have to sleep with Susan, the daughter who disliked me most. But I didn't have a choice, so I went along with Donald's new plan and hoped that the morning would come quickly.

Miraculously, Susan didn't pinch me during the night or kick me out of her bed. The fat cow fell asleep as soon as her bloated head hit her pillow. She didn't budge until it was time for me to leave.

**

On Christmas morning, I woke to a slight nudge from Donald. He told me to get up and be ready to leave in a few minutes, as he had to take me to his mother's apartment. Ms. Junie lived in another section of Vandeveer, not too far from mine on Foster Avenue. Although it seemed strange that we were going to her apartment, I didn't question Donald. However, I knew something troubled him. There was a tremor in his voice, and his eyes were damp when he spoke to me.

I washed up, got dressed, and arrived at Ms. Junie's apartment twenty minutes later. As I entered the living room, I noticed most of the people who attended Hazel's party were there. They all looked sad. Some of the women cried while the men consoled them. Aunty Marlene sat by a window in the kitchen with a blank look on her face. I could see her tear-stained cheeks.

I walked over to her, and when I said "Hello," she turned around and hugged me tightly. While holding me, she began to cry. I felt her shaking hard. A minute later, she released her hold.

"Avianna, go and sit down baby. Yuh Uncle Rendall will be here shortly ta come an' get you," she told me.

I sat on Ms. Junie's sofa and listened intently to the different conversations taking place.

"Mother, you should see de car they were traveling in. Ah doh know how anyone survive dat accident. Ah so tired ah telling Alex about driving an' drinking, but he so damn harden. Now look at what happen," I heard Hazel say to her mother. Rose, another sister chimed in.

"If Veronica survives, it will be a miracle. De passenger side of de car crumple up like an accordion. My Gawd. Ah can't believe what Alex gone an' do. Ah can't believe he do dis. If anyting' happen to Veronica, what going an' become of she two children?" she lamented.

"Rose, calm down. Yuh going ta scare Analia an' she doh need dat right now," Marlene said.

Her sister turned her back to me. However, I could hear her sniffles and see that her shoulders were shaking up and down. She was distraught.

These adults always slipped into their heavy Trinidadian accent when they were around each other. But I understood them perfectly. A knot formed in the pit of my stomach as dread overtook me. I sensed that something terrible had happened to my mother. We didn't get along, but I wanted to see her. I wanted my sister. I wanted Uncle Rendall, and at this point, even Alex. I just wanted to be around anyone who had been close to her.

Uncle Rendall finally arrived. He nodded at Ms. Junie, gave Marlene a brief hug, then walked over to where I sat.

"Analia, get yuh coat. We have to leave now," he said flatly. My uncle never greeted me without a smile. He looked angry and didn't make eye contact with me the way he usually did. I said goodbye to everyone and followed him out the front door.

Once we reached outside Ms. Junie's building, he turned to me and said, "Analia, yuh not going straight home. Yuh mother not dere yet." When I asked him where she was, he told me that she'd be home soon.

Uncle Rendall took me to the home of a friend, Barbara Charles, who I had never met before. She lived with her six-year-old daughter in a brownstone in the Bushwick section of Brooklyn. When she answered the door, the first thing I noticed was her serious countenance.

My uncle's other girlfriends were much more attractive. Barbara had a nice shape, but nothing else about her stood out in a good way. She had an ashy complexion. Her prominent brow bones made her eyes look slightly hollow and cold. I studied her chapped lips and thought they could do with a dab of Vaseline. Her legs were bowed, just like Uncle Rendall's.

Barbara's daughter, Cleopatra, was Dougla. She had long, thick, wavy black hair, large brown eyes, and long lashes. The top row of her teeth were bucked in the front from sucking her thumb. Still, she was a pretty copper-skinned girl.

During my brief stay, I did not feel comfortable. Besides showing me where the bathroom was and discussing sleeping arrangements, my host said little to me. I got the impression that Barbara had been inconvenienced and didn't appreciate my uncle leaving me in her care. His decision puzzled me. It would have made more sense for me to stay with one of my mother's friends.

Uncle Rendall left, and I didn't see him again until December 27th. When he finally returned, he had Avianna with him. I couldn't remember being happier to see my baby sister. I took her in my arms and held on to her tightly until she started struggling against my hold. As I put Avianna to sit on a chair, I saw a bandage on her right leg and several band-aids on her arms.

"Aw, Avianna what happened to you?" I asked with concern. Of course, at two years old, she couldn't explain her injuries.

Uncle Rendall and Barbara retreated to her bedroom to talk. I tried to eavesdrop but couldn't hear as their voices were lowered. A few minutes later, they both reappeared. Barbara handed me my coat, then Uncle Rendall, Avianna, and I left her apartment.

Chapter 24

DEEP SLEEP

Uncle Rendall rang our doorbell. To my surprise, Granny
Clarinda answered the door. She bent down to give Avianna
and me a kiss on each of our cheeks.

"Analia, yuh' alright?" she asked in her Bajan accent.

"Hi Granny, I'm fine," I answered as I walked into our
crowded living room.

I saw a host of my mother's friends and relatives, including
Uncle Errol, Orlando, my grandmother's sister Gladys, my great
uncle George, Aunty Lorraine, her sisters, and Aunty Marlene.

Alex stood by the living room window, leaning on crutches,
smoking a cigarette. I went over to him and said, "Merry
Christmas." He kissed my cheek and asked how I was doing. I
told him I was okay but that I wanted to see my mother. He
looked at me briefly, then hobbled to where Marlene sat on our
sofa.

Aunty Lorraine came over to where I was left standing by
Alex and hugged me. "Hi, baby. How you doin'? Come with me

for a minute. I need to talk to you about something." I followed as she walked into our bedroom. We both sat on the bed, and she began to tell me about a car accident.

Alex, Avianna, and my mom went to Hazel's party but did not arrive until one-thirty Christmas morning. At four o'clock, they decided to leave. Three other friends asked Alex if he would give them a ride home, which he agreed to do. Although he drank excessively throughout the night, neither his siblings nor my mother thought to stop him from driving while intoxicated. Veronica got in the front passenger seat with Avianna on her lap, and the other adults sat in the back.

As Alex drove down Atlantic Avenue, the car hit a patch of ice. He lost control and crashed into one of the pillars holding up the El train tracks. Everyone except my mother walked away from the accident. When the car hit the pillar, she was ejected through the windshield and suffered severe head injuries. Aunty Lorraine explained that Mummy was in a coma, and her doctors were trying their best to make her better.

Relief washed over me as I finally learned the truth about what happened to my mother. Everyone knew of the accident, including Uncle Rendall but chose to keep me in the dark. Aunty Lorraine was the only one who thought I had a right to know.

**

The next evening, I went to Cumberland Hospital with family and friends to visit my mother. I watched as Jamaican Marlene exited an elevator. She walked over to where I sat with Granny and Aunty Gladys.

"Hi, Analia. 'Ow yuh doing love?" she asked while motioning for me to stand up and sit on her lap instead of the chair I occupied.

"I'm good," I replied, even though I felt confused and anxious.

"I just saw your mom, an' I spent quite some time talking wid 'er. Even though 'er eyes are closed, when I asked 'er to squeeze my hand if she could hear what ah was sayin', guess what 'appen? She squeezed it! This is fantastic because it means she gettin' better an' hopefully she'll be home soon okay?"

Marlene was a nurse by profession. In my mind, she had to be telling me the truth about my mom getting better. I began to feel upbeat.

Uncle Rendall glanced over at us and called me to him. We walked to the front desk and waited while the receptionist finished assisting another visitor. He asked her for a pass to see Veronica Edmonds, but she politely told him that children were not allowed on the intensive care ward. Just as we turned away, my mother's attending physician appeared.

"Dr. McIntosh, yuh think it would be possible for my niece to see her mother?" he asked.

"Mr. Walton, we do not allow minors to visit patients who are in ICU. Not only is it dangerous for children, but their reaction to seeing their loved ones can be stressful for the patient. I'm sorry, but I cannot make an exception," the doctor replied.

My uncle looked slightly annoyed but had no choice but to abide by the hospital's rules. I returned to my seat in the lobby and waited patiently for everyone else to visit my mother. She was just a few floors away from me, yet I wasn't allowed to see her. I wanted to cry.

I felt desolate and needed to be with my mom. She had been strict and harsh on me at times, but she was all I had. Sure, Uncle Rendall and Aunty Lorraine had become an integral part of my life. However, no one could replace my mother. It was in the lobby of Cumberland hospital that I realized how much she meant to me.

During the next few days, when relatives and friends weren't at the hospital visiting her, they waited at our apartment for news of her condition. And for the first time ever, my grandmother's mean facial expression was replaced by one that exposed her vulnerability. It must have been hard for Clarinda, knowing that her only daughter was on the brink of death.

Chapter 25

SHE'S GONE

In the predawn hours of New Year's Day, 1973, Uncle Rendall strode into our bedroom and said, "Mammy, Veronica just died." I watched through squinted eyes as a melancholy scene began to unfold.

My grandmother began to wail as she jumped out of the bed that she had been sharing with Avianna and me.

"Oh, Lord! Meh daughter gone! Meh only daughter! Oh God, why? Veronica! Veronica! Ah want meh daughter," she cried.

Uncle Errol had been sleeping on the cot in the living room. Uncle Rendall must have given him the news before telling Granny. He walked over to his mother, held her in his arms, and attempted to console her. A minute or so passed before he started to cry as well.

Uncle Rendall looked tense and appeared to be fighting to keep control of his emotions. Eventually, he said, "Mammy, hush. Yuh going ta wake up Analia, and I don't want her to know as yet."

Granny and Uncle Errol continued to cry. They could not contain their tears. I sat up, then reached for my grandmother and hugged her. Words escaped me. Uncle Rendall sat on the edge of our bed and stared into space. Avianna continued to sleep.

My mother, who recently celebrated her twenty-ninth birthday on December 7th, 1972, died on January 1st, 1973. She left behind two children: one who had just turned two years old the previous month and the other eight years of age.

Later that morning, a steady stream of visitors came to our apartment. As soon as they walked through the door and saw Avianna or me, they started crying and asked the same rhetorical question: How could my mother be dead? When Aunty Lorraine walked in, it was clear that she had been crying and was visibly shaken.

"Analia, sweetheart. Come here baby. I love you, and I'm going to be right here for you and Avianna," she said. I wrapped my arms around her neck and squeezed her tight. I felt her tremble. An immense sense of sorrow floated in the air, and the weight of it all became unbearable. Sadness echoed on the faces of the many individuals who were milling around, crying. I desperately wanted to get out of there.

Alex came by at ten o'clock. Despair washed across his face. I felt sorry for him. It was evident that everyone in the room held him responsible for the accident. As he settled into a chair in the living room, my grandmother ripped into him.

"You kill meh only daughter yuh blasted drunk! Why de hell yuh would drive a car knowing yuh was drinking? Yuh murder meh daughter yuh sonofabitch! You's a murderer! A murderer! Yuh hear me?" she shrieked at him.

Uncle Rendall went over to his mother and tried to calm her down.

"Mammy, stop. Yuh only making everyone feel worse. Carrying on like this isn't going ta bring Veronica back."

My grandmother didn't want to hear what he had to say.

"What shit yuh tryin' ta tell me Rendall? You feel dis rahted bitch had de right ta kill my chile an' get away with it? You feel dize okay? Yuh must be fuckin' crazy!"

Uncle Rendall walked away, shaking his head, and left my grandmother to continue her tirade.

Once again, Aunty Lorraine pulled me aside and tried to explain what happened from a biblical standpoint. She told me that when everyone was born, God already decided the day they would die. However, when a person died, they weren't dead but in a deep sleep. She explained that when the time was right, God would wake up all of the people in that deep sleep, and all of us would live together in heaven.

Aunty Lorraine asked me not to blame Alex for Mum dying. She said people make mistakes, and he would have to live with this one for the rest of his life.

"Promise me you will not hold anything against him, Analia. Remember there is a God, and he is in control."

I didn't understand everything she told me. And I do not know where I found the empathy, but I felt awful for Alex. I decided that I wouldn't be cold towards him or treat him as my grandmother had done.

***

Later that evening, as visitors began to leave, I reveled in the extra breathing room. For most of the day, the overcrowded apartment gave us little space to maneuver.

Just when I thought things were going to calm down a bit,

the doorbell rang. I answered it thinking that one of our guests had left something behind. When I opened the door, there stood Aunty Margaret. I couldn't believe she was in front of me. I stepped into her open arms. Jackie, Gillian, and Patsy, three of her daughters, were standing next to her with broad smiles on their faces. Aunty Margaret bent down to my level and asked me in a whisper if my mother was inside.

"Mummy died, Aunty Margaret." She frowned.

"Analia, what kind of joke yuh playin'? Dat is not a nice ting ta say at all. Suppose it happen fuh real. What yuh would do?" This was going to be tough.

"Aunty Margaret, I'm not lying. Mummy *is* dead," I replied.

"Look, little girl. Go an' tell her dat someone is here ta see her but don't let her know is me."

Uncle Rendall came over to find out who I was speaking with. When Margaret saw him, the look on his face told her that something was wrong.

"Rendall, how yuh doin' love? Where meh girl? Veronica knew dat ah was planning on comin' fuh a visit, but I ain't tell her ah would be here fuh New Years. Ah wanted ta surprise her. Where is she?"

My uncle took a deep breath and said, "Margaret, Veronica passed away dis morning."

She looked at him in disbelief. "What? What yuh talkin' about? Doh talk shit, Rendall! Doh talk shit! Veronica can't be dead!" She barged into the apartment, saw my grandmother, Uncle Errol, and the few remaining friends with grief written all over their faces. The truth hit her.

Aunty Margaret responded with more hysterics than Granny. She dropped to her knees, calling my mother's name.

"Veronica, no! No! you can't be dead. Oh God, no! How she could be dead? Please! Somebody, tell meh! How my darling friend could be dead?" she asked to no one in particular. Both of my uncles attempted to pick her up, but she would not budge. Her daughters were frightened and started to cry as well.

Uncle Rendall finally managed to get Margaret to her feet and walked her to our armchair. She sat down and continued to sob. It took my mother's friend a long time to calm down. Once she did, they told her all about the injuries Mummy sustained, which led to her death. Aunty Margaret stayed with us until the wee hours of the morning. The next time I saw her was at my mother's funeral.

Chapter 26

CURLS AND PINK LACE

Uncle Rendall, Errol, and Aunty Lorraine spent much of their time making funeral arrangements during the following days. They also contacted other friends and family members to inform them of my mother's demise. There was still no word from my father or any of my relatives living in England. It appeared that no one from our former life even cared that Veronica had died. Victor's absence puzzled everyone. *What was going on with him?*

The day before Mummy's service, Uncle Rendall and Granny had a heated argument about whether I should attend the funeral. My grandmother didn't want me to go because, as she put it, "Dat would scar she fuh life!" Uncle Rendall thought I had a right to see my mother for what would amount to the last time. He suggested that they leave the decision up to me.

I sat in the living room with them, but they talked as if I weren't there. Eventually, my uncle turned to me and asked, "Analia, yuh want ta go ta your mother's funeral, or yuh prefer ta stay home?"

My grandmother gave me a look, which I ignored. "I want to go. I want to see Mum."

Granny rolled her eyes and mumbled, "You only agreeing ta go 'cause dat is what Rendall want."

Not true. Why should everyone else get to say goodbye to my mother except me? Uncle Rendall's "wants" had nothing to do with mine.

The funeral service of Veronica Carmen Edmonds took place on January 6, 1973, at Wilkinsons Funeral Home in Brooklyn. I traveled to the parlor in a black limousine with my grandmother, two uncles, and Aunty Lorraine. Avianna remained at home with Mary. When we arrived, many of my mother's friends were in the foyer. The room where her casket rested was filled to standing-room-only capacity. As I walked down the aisle with my uncle towards my seat in the front row, I heard gasps and the sound of people crying. I sat down and stared straight ahead at the box that held my mother's body. While the director officiated, I looked neither to the left or right of the room.

Shortly before the service ended, the funeral director invited anyone who wanted to view my mother for the last time, to come forward. I watched them stop in front of the casket, look at her for a few moments, make the sign of the cross, and then walk away. Many people were bawling by the time that they saw her.

Granny, whose cries could be heard throughout the entire funeral home, fainted and had to be revived with smelling salts. When she came to, she kept repeating the same thing over and over again. "Oh God! My daughter gone! Veronica! Oh God! My only daughter gone!"

Uncle Rendall put his arm around my shoulders and asked if I wanted to go up to the casket. I told him that I did. He and Aunty Lorraine escorted me to the front. I peered into the box and saw my mother for the first time in almost two weeks. She did not look dead to me. If I had not known better, I would have thought she was sleeping. Veronica had on a pink lace dress with a high collar. It looked nice, but it wasn't her style.

The next thing I noticed about my mom was her hair. It hadn't been combed in one of her usual styles. Instead, she wore a curly wig. A craniectomy had been performed on her, resulting in one side of her head being shaved. Aunty Lorraine and Uncle Rendall thought it would be best to have her wear a wig.

I stood in front of my mother's casket, taking in her peaceful countenance. I studied the features that attributed to her beauty and the familiar creases around the corners of her mouth. After resting my eyes on Veronica for the last time, I turned around and walked back to my seat. I often recall the mental picture of her laying in her casket. It is one that I have never forgotten.

Aunty Margaret came over to where I sat and pulled me into an embrace. I felt her shudder as she began to cry. I got emotional, broke down, and cried with her. Aunty Marlene told Margaret to let me go. "Hear nuh. Ah know yuh upset, but all a dat crying' on Analia, isn't going ta do her any good," she stated.

We left the funeral parlor and drove to the burial site at Woodland Cemetery in Staten Island. Everyone gathered around my mother's plot. A priest read a few verses from the bible and said a prayer. Then we were given flowers to throw on top of her casket, which was lowered to the ground.

Many years later, I learned that a headstone had never been placed on my mother's grave. Her brothers either could not or would not put money towards one. Because of their inaction, Avianna and I would never be able to visit our mother's final resting place or put flowers by her headstone on special occasions if we chose to do so.

Had the roles been reversed, Veronica Edmonds would have handled the situation differently. Although she had been giving when alive, her extended generosity was not reciprocated at a time when her family needed it most. But I couldn't place all of the blame for her not having a headstone on my uncles. Victor Edmonds never showed up. He too shirked his responsibilities to his wife.

When we returned home, several trays of food and desserts were on the kitchen counter, which Ms. Mary and several of our neighbors made for my mother's repast. Aunty Lorraine also had several dishes delivered from one of her favorite restaurants. The eating, drinking, and conversation provided a brief respite from the sad event that had taken place earlier in the day.

I heard several people ask my grandmother when she planned to return to London and who would care for Avianna and me.

"De girls gone' stay here wid Rendall until we fine out what Victor want ta do," she informed them.

At the mention of my father's name, my heart skipped a beat. He had to be on his way to get us. After all, with Mum gone, Avianna and I needed him now more than ever. Unknown to me, Victor was going through some changes of his own: changes that would alienate him from us for a long time. Changes that left us in the hands of strangers and family who did not have the interests of Avianna and me at heart.

Chapter 27

24 SUYDAM STREET

My grandmother, Orlando, and Uncle Errol stayed with us for a week after the funeral. During that time, I didn't see or hear from Alex. However, Aunty Lorraine, Aunty Marlene, and Ms. Cynthia stopped by every evening. They helped my grandmother sort through my mother's clothes and other belongings and decided what would be kept or given away.

While handling this task, they avoided talking about the accident. It seemed as though Veronica was dead for much longer than two weeks, and what had recently transpired was old news.

Granny often asked me whether or not I wanted to go back to England to live with her. She emphasized that Avianna and I did not have to stay with Uncle Rendall. It would be perfectly fine if we wanted to be with her. I didn't know how to respond to her question. Part of me wanted to go because I would be closer to my dad, Aunty Annette, and the rest of my U.K. family. On the other hand, I didn't want to betray Uncle Rendall by leaving him.

In the end, I decided to stay. Living in our apartment and going to school with all of my friends wouldn't be so bad. Even though Mummy wasn't around, at least I could remain in the last home that we shared. I'd sleep in the same bed that she slept in, sit on the same chairs she sat on, and eat on the same dinnerware she ate from. And I could use the same cutlery that once touched her mouth. Somehow, I would remain connected to my mother.

In retrospect, a weighty decision about whom I wanted to live with should not have been left up to me, a minor, to make. Avianna and I needed female guidance in our lives. Uncle Rendall, a twenty-four-year-old man, was separated from his wife, lived a carefree life, and ran around with a stash of women. He didn't have a clue about raising children, never mind young girls. Despite these facts, no one in the family raised any objections to Avianna and me living with him. I guess they all felt that since my father hadn't shown any interest in our welfare and Uncle Rendall offered to step up to the plate, why not let him?

My grandmother and Orlando returned to England on January 14, 1973. Uncle Errol went home to Wisconsin a day later. While I was a little sad to see them go, we didn't share any teary goodbyes.

I longed to get settled once again and move on with my life. I wanted to return to school, hang out with my friends, and do all of the fun stuff I had engaged in before my mother died. I was also ready to take on my role as Avianna's big sister with renewed vigor. The talk I had with my father the night before we left England came to my mind. I made a silent promise to him and Avianna that I would do my best to take care of her going forward.

After dropping Uncle Errol off at the airport, Uncle Rendall,

Avianna, and I returned to our apartment. Once we got there, he told me to pack all of my clothes and Avianna's in our suitcases.

"Are we going on a trip somewhere?" I asked.

"No. You're going ta live in a new house wid a friend of mine. Do you remember Barbara? She's the lady you spent some time with a few weeks ago." He spoke as if nothing unusual was taking place.

"You mean the one I stayed with on Christmas morning?" I asked.

"Yes. Well anyway, she's going ta take care of you and Avianna fuh me since I have ta work. Don't worry though. I'll be around ta check on you." My uncle told me this with a certain finality in his voice, leaving no room for further questioning. Had I known we would not live with him, I would have returned to London with Granny.

My concerns were justified. Uncle Rendall's visits to "check" on Avianna and I were far and few between. Because of his absence and the financial pressure on Barbara, my role as a big sister went to another level. The fictional character Cinderella and I had more in common than I would have liked.

**

Less than three weeks after losing our mother, my sister and I were placed in the home of a woman whom we barely knew. Along with her daughter, she now had two additional children in her care. Knowing my uncle, he probably sold her a sob story that included him being the only relative who cared about our welfare. That if it was not for him, we would be placed in "the system," and being the honorable gentleman that he was, he could not let that happen. Then he'd play on her emotions, ask her to help him avoid losing his nieces, with a promise that he'd settle down with her and they could raise Avianna, Cleo and me, together.

In the meantime, I was going through the first of many bouts of deja vu. Once again, I left behind all that I had become comfortable with. The apartment I lived in with my mother, my friends in the projects at P.S. 269, and anything else associated with my past life.

Barbara's home, with its' depressing aura, saddened me. And to make matters worse, even though we recently lost our mother, she showed no empathy towards Avianna and me. Not one warm smile. Not one word of comfort. Not one hug. The lady of the house was not a happy person. She always seemed to be mad at the world and rarely smiled. When she did, my uncle's visits usually had something to do with the slight change in her demeanor. But it wasn't her lack of empathy that unnerved me. It was the way that I'd often catch her staring at me with those cold, sunken eyes of hers.

We were informed that Avianna, Cleo, and I were to share one bedroom, one closet, and one bed. I resented those sleeping arrangements. Cleo wet the bed, and not one night passed when she didn't grace us with a urine bath.

I was disgusted by the feel of her pee wetting my nightclothes. All I could do was to inch as close as possible to the wall on my side of the bed with Avianna right up under me. In the morning, we'd pull the blanket off the bed to let the air dry the wet sheets. After a night or two, they'd acquire a pissy scent as Barbara only changed them on weekends.

She found a babysitter, Shirley, for Avianna, who resided a few doors down from us. Shirley lived with a boatload of other relatives. Although her house was always crowded, Barbara seemed to trust her. Avianna stayed with Shirley and her family until I got home from school and picked her up.

Uncle Rendall enrolled me in Public School 274. Once again, I went through the routine of making new friends and explaining the reason for my "funny accent." I was wary of the folk on this side of town. They were different, much rougher around the edges, and suspicious of everyone and everything.

I liked my new teachers, and they were fond of me. I impressed them with my reading skills and ability to speak "proper" English. My British accent endeared me to them even more.

I met some kids on our block and introduced myself as Christine Elizabeth Edmonds. I lied about my name as I wanted to feel accepted amongst the Donnas', Sharons', and Cheryls' of the world. I was tired of getting weird looks whenever I told anyone outside of our family circle mine and Avianna's names.

Two weeks passed before we saw Uncle Rendall again. When he appeared, he announced he was going to cut my hair. I didn't care one way or another. However, once the deed was done, I fell in love with my afro. Uncle Rendall bought me Afro Sheen products, which included shampoo, hair grease, and hairspray. I used them religiously and made sure that my hair always looked neat.

Initially, my hair was too soft and lacked the volume needed for a Michael Jackson afro. But the more I slept with it out, the fuller it began to look. Soon, I became known as the girl with the best afro in our school and neighborhood.

On windy days, I hated the unwanted parts that the wind made in my fro, so I mastered the art of quickly turning my head in the opposite direction of the wind so it wouldn't mess up my hair. And if by chance, my afro blew out of shape, as soon as I arrived at my destination, I went to the nearest restroom to fix it.

Chapter 28

BUSHWICK

Life with Barbara on Suydam Street was nothing like I imagined. Since she worked from three to eleven o'clock at night at a data processing center, I had to make sure that everything ran smoothly at home during the evening. When I lived with my mother, of course, I had chores, but Barbara's expectations were a bit much for an eight-year-old.

Cleo and I went to different schools. At the end of my school day, I had to walk four blocks to hers, pick her up, get Avianna from the babysitter, help Cleo with her homework while completing mine, warm and serve dinner or prepare something for us to eat if nothing was ready. I also tidied the place, bathed the girls, and put them to bed.

As with everything else, I adjusted. But there were many times when I wanted to be engaging in activities like other normal children. I couldn't go outside to play during the week unless I had finished all my chores and took Avianna and Cleo with me. It wasn't any fun playing tag or dodge ball with your friends while trying to keep your eyes on two younger children.

When Uncle Rendall visited, I wasn't sure whether or not he could tell how unhappy I was or if he chose to ignore my beseeching looks. I often asked him to take Avianna and me home with him, but he left us at Barbara's despite my pleas.

Uncle Rendall changed. The love and concern he showed towards us when my mother was alive disappeared. His new attitude perturbed me.

I also found his reluctance to contact Aunty Lorraine, Marlene, Alex, or Ms. Cynthia troubling. I told him several times that I wanted to call and let them know where Avianna and I stayed. His response was always the same; "Listen, ah doh want anybody ta know where you are right now. Just concentrate on getting settled, an' once you do, we'll call dem. Those people doh mean you good anyway, so you might as well forget about them."

Uncle Rendall's change of heart towards the people he had been close to surprised me. He had dated Aunty Marlene, flirted openly with Aunty Lorraine, and knew Ms. Cynthia well. I assumed he liked them.

"Aunty Lorraine was always good to Avianna and me. Why would you say that about her?" And wasn't Aunty Marlene your girlfriend too?" I asked him. I had struck a nerve.

"Analia, watch yuh mouth and don't talk about my other women friends when Barbara is in the house. What's wrong with you?" he replied.

I didn't let up. "Please call Aunty Lorraine. I miss her."

He became exasperated. "Alright, alright. I'll call her soon."

Once again, I would have to wait until he was good and ready, and God only knew how long that would take.

***

Eventually, there were longer lapses of time between Uncle Rendall's visits. His absence took a toll on Barbara. I thought it impossible for her to become any more solemn or moody, but sure enough, she did, and I was on the receiving end of her stress.

"Analia, why yuh didn't put de butter back in de fridge?"

"Where de hell is meh afro comb?"

"Why yuh didn't change de sheets on de bed?"

"Why yuh let Avianna spill juice on her clothes?"

"Why isn't Cleopatra's homework finished?"

"Why yuh didn't make sure she put her wet pajamas in de tub to be washed?"

Goodness! She acted as though I was a grown-ass woman, and these were my children.

My situation lightened up a little when Uncle Rendall spent the night. Barbara was more amenable with him around and didn't bark at me as much. The permanent frown she wore for most of the time slowly dissipated, and she seemed more open, more talkative.

There wasn't a door that divided her room from ours, so I always knew when Barbara got serviced by my uncle. She wasn't noisy, and instead of calling his name, she hissed. I think her low-keyed response to sex was indicative of her cold personality. In either case, I got a kick out of listening to them do "it."

Sometimes, when I felt mischievous, I attempted to shake Cleo awake to hear her mother, but that was like trying to bring a dead person to life. On the odd occasion when I managed to wake her up, she was so damn lethargic that you'd think she smoked weed.

***

On February 6, 1973, I turned nine. My birthday came and went without fanfare, which was a far cry from what I had been accustomed to.

I didn't receive a card, cake, or presents, nor did I hear from Uncle Rendall.

One Saturday afternoon, the doorbell rang. When Barbara answered it, I heard a familiar voice.

"Hi Barbara, my name is Lorraine. I'm a good friend of Veronica's. Rendall told me I could come by to see Analia and Avianna."

Aunty Lorraine was finally here! I ran to the door, slipped past Barbara, and leaped into her arms. She started crying and laughing at the same time. Clearly, we were both ecstatic to see each other.

"Hi, baby. How are you? Oh, it's so good to see you, Analia! Where's Avianna?" As we walked into the living room, Barbara motioned for Aunty Lorraine to sit down and offered her a drink. "No thanks, Barbara. I'm good for now," she told her superficially gracious host.

Just then, my baby sister stepped into the room.

"Avianna, look at you," she exclaimed. "You're getting so big. Come here and give Aunty Lorraine a hug!"

She and Barbara began a conversation, and I learned a lot about my "caretaker" as I listened in on their talk. I found out that she immigrated from Trinidad, was married but currently separated from Cleo's father, who lived in California. I also found out she had begun dating Uncle Rendall only a few months before my mother's accident.

They spoke for a long time, but I didn't mind. I was happy to have Aunty Lorraine in our presence. Avianna and I sat on her lap while she told Barbara about her close relationship with our mother and us. She also mentioned how upset she was with Uncle Rendall for not letting anyone know where we were. So many people were wondering what had happened to Veronica's daughters.

Barbara seemed uncomfortable with the direction the conversation had taken. But she seized the opportunity to shed some light on her current predicament.

"Lorraine, I don't know what ta say. Sometimes Rendall does show up. But most of de time, he's not around. Weeks have gone by without him giving me anything for dese girls and ah struggling just like everyone else."

Aunty Lorraine looked at her with one of her penetrating gazes.

"Barbara, you mean to tell me it didn't dawn on you to ask Rendall if the girls would want to see any of Veronica's friends? You didn't think to ask if there were certain people they should stay in contact with?"

The line of questions put Barbara on the spot. She simply replied, "No, not really. I felt that was up to Rendall."

"Well, let me give you my home and work numbers so we can keep in touch. I'd also like to have the girls over for the weekend as soon as possible, if that's alright with you," Lorraine asked.

"No problem. I'm sure Analia would love that." What an understatement! I could not contain the huge smile that spread across my face as I thought about the possibility of getting away from Barbara and Cleo for a while.

Chapter 29

FAMILIAR TERRITORY

A few weeks later, Aunty Lorraine took Avianna and me home to spend the weekend with her. Everyone at the Marcy Projects was so happy to see us.

As usual, we had a fun-filled weekend that included going to the movies to see Charlotte's Web and shopping for clothes, shoes, and hair accessories. It felt good to be back on this side of town with people who cared about my sister and me.

Sunday came way too fast, and before I knew it, the time had come for us to return home. When Aunty Lorraine asked me to get our coats, I began to cry.

"Analia, what's the matter baby? Why are you crying? You're going to see me soon. I promise. I'll never lose contact with you again. Come on sweetheart, stop crying. It can't be that bad living with Barbara."

"Yes, it is!" I sobbed.

"What do you mean?" she asked.

I told her about all the chores Barbara made me do and

her bad mood when weeks went by, without a visit from Uncle Rendall.

"Aunty Lorraine, I never get to have fun anymore. I'm always cleaning the apartment and taking care of Cleo and Avianna."

"Well, honey. You're Avianna's big sister, and she needs you to look out for her."

"I do look out for her. But it's all of the other stuff I have to do that bothers me."

"Stuff like what?" she asked.

I didn't respond right away.

"Come on baby. Tell me. Stuff like what?" Aunty Lorraine coaxed.

"I have to pick Cleo up from school, get Avianna from the babysitter, make sure that they eat dinner, and sometimes, I even have to fix something to go with the meat or fish, which Barbara cooks. I also have to help Cleo with her homework, bathe Avianna, and then get both of them ready for bed." My godmother got angry.

"You have got to be kidding me. Barbara has you doin' all of that? She must be out of her ever-lovin' mind! You wait until I see Rendall. Ima give him a piece of my damn mind. He can't have you livin' like this!"

I panicked. "Please don't say anything to them. If you do, they're going to be upset with me. And they won't let me see you anymore."

Aunty Lorraine shook her head in disgust. "I don't like what I'm hearing. But I don't want you to get in trouble either. So I won't say anything – for now. If things get worse, you have to let me know. In the meantime, I promise I'll come and get you and Avianna as much as possible, okay?"

Telling someone about my situation at home made me feel slightly better. Who better to share my woes with than Aunty Lorraine? I knew that she would keep her promise, and knowing that she planned to see us more often, gave me something to look forward to.

After we had been dropped off, Barbara scavenged through our bags. Although my godmother had been thoughtful enough to buy a few outfits for Cleo, Barbara still felt slighted. She made me hang our outfits in the closet and leave them there. I was forbidden to wear any of my new clothes or shoes to school.

I wore different outfits on Monday, Tuesday, and Wednesday. But on Thursdays and Friday, I had to wear the clothes I wore on Monday and Tuesday – again. This rotation was embarrassing. My classmates noticed, and I felt as though a bullseye had been placed on my chest. Although Barbara adamantly refused to let me wear any new outfits, thankfully, that same restriction did not apply to Avianna.

***

Occasionally, Uncle Rendall took us to visit his other women. I loved it when we spent time together without Cleo tagging along. She was not a part of our former life, and I didn't want to share any of it with her.

On one of these occasions, we met his latest acquisition, a pretty woman named Deborah Brady. She looked like one of the women I saw on the front covers of the Jet Magazine; tall, curvy, and stylishly dressed. Deborah wore thick prescription glasses, but her cocoa complexion, deep almond eyes, and curly, thick lashes complemented her beautiful face. Deborah liked wearing her hair pulled back into an afro puff at the nape of her neck with strands of baby hair slicked down along her hairline. She was the only woman he dated that I became attached to and adored.

Deborah's mother, Gina, worked with my uncle at the Department of Labor and was unhappy about her daughter dating Rendall Walton. She saw many of his girlfriends visit him at the office and knew that he was a womanizer. Although she tried to warn Deborah about his philandering ways, Gina's advice was ignored.

Before long, we were allowed to spend a weekend with Deborah and her family. The Brady's resided in the Jefferson Houses located in East Harlem, NY. The cluster of buildings spread over several blocks reminded me of those in the Vandeveer and Marcy Projects. One visible difference was the light-colored bricks. They seemed to brighten the environment.

Deborah shared a three-bedroom apartment on the 7th floor of their building with her parents and younger brother George. I enjoyed being around this family because of the warmth and friendliness they extended towards Avianna and me. They, along with their neighbors, took an immediate liking to us. The fact that we were young children who had recently lost their mother garnered a lot of sympathy. Our loss also recalled the blessing of having their loved ones still alive.

Uncle Rendall had no reservations about us spending time with Deborah. He knew that if she developed a close relationship with us, he would eventually succeed in working his way into her bed. I didn't care about his ulterior motive. I was just thrilled to have another woman in my life who was as nice to us as Aunty Lorraine. Someone who was unlike Barbara.

On our second visit to her apartment, I made the mistake of wearing my newest pair of reject sneakers. The same kind that I had been teased for at school when I first arrived from London. Deborah looked at my cheaply made footwear and went off on my uncle.

"Rendall! Why do you have Analia in these tore up sneakers? Are you crazy?" she asked.

Uncle Rendall was not pleased with her verbal assault. "Deborah, hush. There isn't anything wrong with her sneakers. Ah jus' buy them for her."

"Oh give me a break! You can't have the poor girl going to school in those reject shoes. All the other kids are gonna tease her." She turned to me and said, "Analia, I'll take you shopping for some Pro-Keds. And if that coconut you live with don't let you wear them, let me know."

My heart skipped a beat. *Did I hear Deborah correctly? Was she going to buy me some*

Pro-Keds? I was finally going to get a pair. I couldn't wait.

"Do whatever you want. Just stop interrogating me. If you want to spend thirteen dollars on some sneakers, go right on ahead 'cause I'm not buying them," Uncle Rendall replied.

She rolled her eyes. "Yeah, I know. You won't spend money on some decent sneakers because you're too damn cheap! You shouldn't be so tight when it comes to your nieces."

Deborah was right. I began to recognize my uncle's miserly ways, a trait I had never witnessed before. He seemed generous when my mother was alive, but once she died, a new man emerged.

If I asked him for a dime to buy something from the corner store, he gave me a nickel. If I asked him to buy Captain Crunch cereal, he bought Cornflakes. If I asked for Hostess bakery products, he responded, "No. You don't need to be eating that stuff." The man who once bought three different kinds of cereal for his favorite niece was gone.

Thank goodness for Deborah. She kept her word and bought me a pair of navy blue Pro-Keds. I wore those sneakers everywhere and with everything. I wore them with play clothes, school clothes and going out clothes. I wore those Keds until they started leaning to one side, and the rubber wore out at the heel. When it looked like they were hanging together by a thread, I finally had to throw them away. I held onto those sneakers for so long because I knew that I wouldn't get new Pro-Keds any time soon unless a benefactor bought another pair.

Deborah dressed like a runway model and expected everyone around her to do the same. She took us shopping at Macy's and A & S and bought us clothes in the latest fashion. Our time spent with her was filled with a lot of activity. We went to the movies, ice-skating, and events that took place in her neighborhood. We'd go to Central Park, rent bikes, and ride for hours. We always did something fun and never had a dull moment when hanging out with the Brady family.

Chapter 30

CINDERELLA AND HER FRIED FISH

Barbara finally let me wear one of my new outfits to school. I received several compliments and, for a change, felt good about how I looked. To prove that I had more nice clothes, I invited Suzette, one of the best dressers in our school, to come home with me. I knew I would be in trouble if Barbara found out, so I swore Cleo to secrecy. I threatened to tell her friends that she wet the bed if she snitched on me for good measure. I was confident that she wouldn't say a word.

Suzette was one of my closest friends. The fact that I didn't dress as well as her did not stop our friendship from blossoming. Her mom made the tastiest tuna fish sandwiches for lunch, which she often exchanged with me for my peanut butter and jelly. Her preference for PB&J over tuna was lost on me. But I happily obliged because we didn't eat tuna fish at home.

When my friend saw all of the clothes I had with tags on them, she couldn't believe it. "Wow, Analia! You got a lot of stuff. How come you don't wear these nice outfits to school?" she asked.

"My Aunt won't let me. She says I have to save my new stuff for when we go out," I replied.

"Dag, how stupid! They shouldn't make you dress the way you do when you have all of these nice clothes."

I relished the opportunity to show Suzette my wardrobe. I knew that she would tell everyone in our homeroom about my clothes, which is precisely what I wanted. At least they'd know that I had nice gear just like them.

The issue with my outfits and the many chores assigned to me were not the only reasons I disliked living under Barbara's roof. I also had to endure spending damn near every Sunday at church with her mother, Ms. Gordon, a religious fanatic who scared me. After getting to know this woman, I realized that my "guardian" was a replica of her mother. The two of them were simply unlikeable.

Sunday service at Shiloh Baptist Church lasted all day. Cleo and I had to take part in a strange ceremony that always freaked us out. Along with the other women in the congregation, we had to wear long white dresses with our heads wrapped in white turbans. As a heavy cloud of incense permeated the air, congregants twirled us around and repeated nonsensical chants. We watched in horror as some caught the holy ghost, spoke in tongues, and collapsed on the floor. The entire experience was unsettling and made Sundays the worst day of our week.

Although we attended a Baptist church with Ms. Gordon, my uncle had Avianna, and I baptized in a Roman Catholic Church. He didn't ask Aunty Lorraine or Ms. Cynthia to sponsor us officially. Instead, he chose Barbara and Uncle Roland to be our godparents. My mother would not have given the honor to either one of them.

I went on living my "new life" and adjusted to carrying out

my Suzie Homemaker duties. I tried my best to avoid getting on Barbara's bad side. However, there were a few times when I messed up.

Once, I left my keys inside the apartment, and it wasn't until I got home after school that I realized what I had done. Rather than wait for Barbara to get home or call Uncle Rendall, I shimmied up the drainpipe, climbed through an unlocked window in our bedroom, and opened the door. I didn't want the witch to find out that I had neglected to take my keys with me. However, the landlord saw me and asked why I hadn't rung his bell.

"Analia, don't ever climb up the pipe again. You can hurt yourself."

I thought he dropped the matter. I was wrong. When Barbara came home, he told her what I did. In turn, she beat me.

One day after school, I came home to find a note on the kitchen table instructing me to prepare a side dish for dinner. Barbara had stewed some chicken but didn't make anything to go with it. After tidying the place and getting the girls settled, I put potatoes on to boil. Afterward, I went into the living room to watch television.

As is always the case with food when it burns, I didn't smell anything until a smoky scent filled the air. I jumped up, rushed into the kitchen, and saw the rising smoke. I took the pot off the stove and attempted to add water to the burned potatoes. But my inner right arm brushed against the hot metal, causing me to drop the pot. Fortunately, the hot water did not splash on me. The next thought that came to my mind was that Barbara would kill me for wasting her food.

I threw the potatoes in the garbage and tried to scrub the pot as best as I could. When it became apparent that I couldn't get rid of the black stuff at the bottom, I gave up and boiled a second set of potatoes. This time, I stayed in the kitchen and kept an eye on the stove.

Within an hour, a nasty blister developed on my arm. I found some Vaseline in the bathroom cabinet and smeared a good bit of it over the burn. Ouch! It seemed as though the petroleum jelly set my whole arm on fire. Still, I put a band-aid on top of the blister and donned a long-sleeved shirt, which I hoped would hide my wound from Barbara.

When she arrived home from work, the apartment still smelled smoky.

"Analia, why does it smell as if something burned in here?" she asked.

I paused for a minute before responding. "I made a mistake with the food."

"What yuh mean by mistake? I just needed you ta fix something ta go with de chicken."

"I boiled some potatoes for us and burned them."

"How? You wasn't payin' attention ta de pot?" she inquired.

I explained what happened and showed her my arm. She didn't beat me but issued a warning.

"Doh let that happen again. Yuh uncle doesn't give me anything for you and Avianna. Ah struggling ta keep food on de table and ah doh need you wasting what little ah have."

She asked to see my arm. The blister had turned pink and bubbly. She retrieved a tube of antibiotic ointment from her medicine cabinet and put some on my arm. For several days after the incident, she checked my arm to make sure that it was healing. Her act of kindness surprised me. Truthfully, I didn't think she had it in her. To this day, I have an ugly scar that reminds me of the day I burned the potatoes.

Most of the time, I behaved myself and stayed out of trouble. However, occasionally, I acted up and did something out of character. One day, I got the bright idea to fry some of the goldfish Barbara owned. I needed to know whether or not these fish could be fried like those she bought at the supermarket. At least that's what I told myself.

I took a strainer from one of the draws in our kitchen. Even though they did their best to evade me, I scooped out two of the goldfish from the tank. They were so small that I left them in the strainer, which I placed in the kitchen sink. Next, I poured some oil into a frying pan and turned on the stove. When I determined that the oil had gotten hot enough, I placed the two goldfish I had retrieved in the pan. Not less than a few seconds later, the skin on the fish started to crinkle, and before I knew it, they shriveled up. I confirmed via my experiment that goldfish were not meant to be cooked. I threw away what little of them was left, washed the dishes, and put everything back in its place.

A few days later, Uncle Rendall stopped by. While cleaning the tank, I heard him say, "Barbara, what happened to de two goldfish with de little black specks on them?" Oops! I didn't realize that my testers had distinguishing marks.

"I have no idea," she replied.

"Well, yuh better keep an eye on yuh tank. Yuh big fish might be eatin' de smaller ones."

Inwardly I laughed. My evil deed had gone undetected.

Chapter 31

HUMPTY

While living on Suydam Street, I had my first dalliance with romance. A nice-looking boy in my homeroom class named Johnny made it clear that he wanted to go out with me. My suitor reminded me of my mixed-race cousins. He had a fair complexion with blond, curly hair and green eyes. I liked him. He was sweet, well-mannered, and mature for his age. While other boys were pulling the hair of girls they crushed on, Johnny wrote notes to me asking when I would come to his house to meet his older sisters.

"Hey Analia, is it okay if I walk you home from school?" he asked one afternoon.

"I suppose so. But why?"

"Why do you think smarty pants?" he replied with a cute smile.

I invited trouble by granting Johnny's request. Both Barbara and Uncle Rendall would be angry if they found out. But since he was so cute and friendly, I took the risk. Later that afternoon, he waited for me to organize my bookbag. After taking it from me, he carried it until we got to Marilyn's. After doing this a few more times, he asked me to go out with him. I should have known better, but I said yes.

Johnny gave me a Jean Nate gift set with cologne splash and talcum powder. I felt nervous about telling Barbara and Uncle Rendall but decided it would be best to let them know. After I showed them my gift, he asked who had given it to me.

"Johnny, a friend of mine."

"You're too young ta be accepting gifts from boys. Tell him thanks and give him back de gift," Uncle Rendall instructed.

So this is what I got for being honest? I ignored my uncle and kept the set hidden in the back of our closet. Perhaps when I spent the weekend with Aunty Lorraine's or Deborah's, I'd have a chance to use my special toiletries.

Since Barbara worked the night shift at her job, I continued to let Johnny walk me home. Before saying goodbye, he usually asked the same question: "Analia, when will you come to my house?" I told him that I was not allowed to, but he wouldn't give up. "You want one of my sisters to talk to your auntie or uncle? We're not going to do anything except watch TV."

He's just so sweet. "No Johnny. It's not that. My aunt isn't home during the evenings, and there isn't anyone else to pick up my sister from the sitter."

Disappointment washed across his face. "You can't even come over on the weekends?" he pleaded. *He had no idea who I lived with.*

"I'll see what I can do." I knew that Barbara wasn't going to let me go. I told him "I'd see" to give him some hope.

I had another suitor, James, the nephew of Avianna's

babysitter, vying for my affection. He was the complete opposite of Johnny: not cute, mannerly, or mature. If Johnny was a Prince Charming, James was a Humpty Dumpty, fat and squat, with a butt too big for a boy.

Whenever I picked up Avianna, Shirley dutifully reminded me that her egg-shaped nephew had a crush on me. "Christine, James say he wanna' go out wid you. You don't want my nephew for your boyfriend?"

I simply looked at her and smiled, but my insides churned. I could not stomach the thought of going out with that fat boy.

***

I went against my better judgment and finally caved into James' older sister. She constantly pleaded on her brother's behalf and practically begged me to go out with him.

"Come on Christine. James really likes you. He nice an' everything, and he ain't gonna let nobody mess wid you. You should go out with him, at least for a little while."

When I took longer than a minute to respond, she saw that as a positive sign. "So, you gonna go out with him, right?"

As she stood in front of me, I kept thinking, *Johnny or James? James or Johnny? Which one should I choose?* A great idea flashed through my mind. Since James went to a different school, I could go out with him for about two weeks just to get his fat ass off my back. Johnny would never know. *Just two weeks,* I told myself, and then I would dump Humpty.

"Alright, Laura, I'll go out with James."
She smiled broadly.
"James! Christine say she gonna go out wid you. Come outside and talk to her!"

I heard him stumbling down the stairs. Moments later, he stood in front of me panting as if he had just finished a hundred-yard dash. He flashed a grin on his pathetic face.

"Analia, you really gonna go out wid me?" I almost said, "No."

"Yes James. I am."

"Alright then. Wait here, and I'll walk you to your house."

He went inside and returned a few minutes later with several of my favorite candies in his hands. In the right, he held a pack of Banana Now and Laters. In the left, three individually wrapped Swedish Fish.

"Here, these are for you."

I took them, offered a polite "Thank you," and turned around to walk home, hoping he changed his mind about accompanying me.

"Wait up," James said. He closed the front gate to their house, put his heavy arm around my shoulders, and walked me to my front door. If Humpty planned to supply me with Now and Laters and Swedish fish for the next two weeks, we were going to get along fine.

James and I started "going out" with each other on a Thursday, and we broke up the following Tuesday. Why? Because I got busted. He couldn't wait for me to get home from school and just had to show up at P.S. 274 to walk me home. There I was, walking arm in arm with Johnny, when I saw that distinctive, egg-shaped body plodding down the street in our direction.

I tried to pry my arm from Johnny's as James got closer, but he would have none of that. Instead, he pulled me closer to him. I couldn't avoid the inevitable any longer, and when James finally met up with us, I looked him in the eye and said, "Hi."

He gave a slight nod and kept on walking.

I don't know which shortcut he took home, but when I got to the corner of my block, I could see him and most of his relatives standing in front of his house. Johnny walked me to my door, said goodbye, and went home.

I went upstairs and stayed there for about an hour, thinking of something creative to tell James. As hard as I tried, I could not make up a plausible excuse for what he saw. I had put off getting Avianna long enough. I headed down the block to get my sister and prepared myself to face Humpty and his crew.

Laura was the first one to launch an attack.

"Christine! You two timin' my brother? If you didn't wanna go out with him, all you had to do was say so. Now he gonna kick your butt!" she yelled.

"Laura, leave that girl alone. You act like she and James was gonna get married or something. They young kids," Shirley said with a laugh.

But Laura was hurting for her brother.

"I don't care what they was gonna do. She ain't got no business messin' round on James. You know how much he like her."

Shirley looked at me and said, "Analia go 'head and apologize to James. Then come and get your baby sister."

I turned to James, offered a terse apology, took Avianna in my arms, and went home. However, the saga did not end there. My scorned suitor and his family were popular. Everyone on the block felt his pain.

Shortly after our break-up, I came under the attack of James' cross-eyed friend Cheryl. One afternoon, she stood in the middle of the street outside of our brownstone, and in her husky voice, screamed, "Christine! You gonna get yo' butt whipped when you come outside! Christine! Come on downstairs, you cheater!"

Lucky for me, neither Barbara nor Uncle Rendall was home. Had they been, I would have indeed gotten a beating and just not from the idiots outside.

Johnny and I broke up too. Once he found out about James, he dropped me like a hot potato. I understood. What I did was wrong. However, I missed not having him walk me home anymore. I lost him because of Humpty Dumpty, someone who was not my type. Someone I did not like or intend to date in the first place.

Chapter 32

MCDONALD'S

My Uncle Lloyd, who lived in Trinidad, planned to visit us. I overheard Uncle Rendall telling Barbara that his brother would stay with him but spend some time with Avianna and me. I had never met my mother's other brother. I wondered whether he was nice and if he'd like us enough to take us back to Trinidad with him. Anything would be better than living with Barbara and her incontinent daughter.

Uncle Lloyd arrived, and as expected, he came to see us. I have no idea how he found his way to Barbara's apartment on his own, but one day, he was there when I got home from school.

"Oh my gawsh! Look at my beautiful niece! Come here, my darling, and give yuh uncle Lloyd a hug!"

He smothered me with kisses and marveled at how much Avianna resembled his sister.

"Dis'lil' one. My goodness, she looks just like Veronica!" he exclaimed while pointing at Avianna. I liked him instantly.

Uncle Lloyd didn't resemble any of his brothers. He was much taller and slimmer than Uncle Rendall. His complexion and his eyes reminded me of honey; a captivating shade of amber. Even his hair was light brown. Everything about Uncle Lloyd appeared to be golden.

Barbara stood quietly on one side of the living room and observed the interaction between my uncle, Avianna, and me. I'm sure Uncle Lloyd must have wondered how his brother dealt with a woman like her in the world.

"Analia, what yuh would like ta do? Where can I take you all ta have some fun?" Uncle Lloyd asked me.

I wasted no time responding. "Can we go to McDonald's?"

"What is McDonald's?" he asked.

"It's a place where we can get hamburgers, French fries, and milkshakes," I explained.

Uncle Lloyd seemed puzzled. "Why yuh want ta eat there when yuh have home-cooked food? You don't want ta see a movie instead?" he asked.

I refused to be swayed. "No Uncle Lloyd. We prefer to go to McDonald's. I'm sure they'll have something you would like to eat as well."

He laughed and said, "Alright, let's see what dis McDonald's is all about. You know how ta get there?"

"Yes, it isn't far from here. We can walk."

I didn't look at Barbara for fear of seeing a look of disapproval. I took my uncle's hand, led him towards the door, and we left the apartment with Avianna and Cleo.

I could barely contain my excitement upon our arrival at McDonald's. I studied the menu and ordered a Big Mac, Quarter

Pounder with cheese, French fries, a strawberry milkshake, and an apple pie. I didn't know when we'd have another opportunity to try something other than the plain hamburgers, which Uncle Rendall always bought, so I over-ordered. Cleo also wanted a Big Mac and fries. Avianna didn't eat much, but I still had Uncle Lloyd buy her a cheeseburger. He didn't order anything for himself.

As we walked towards an unoccupied table with our two trays of food, I was on top of the world! I got ready to treat my tummy to a delectable McDonald's feast.

After eating some of this gigantic burger, I began to feel nauseous. I couldn't even finish half of the Big Mac! And Cleo struggled to eat hers as well. I felt like heaving at the thought of attempting to consume all the food in front of me.

As Uncle Lloyd watched us eat, he realized that we had taken advantage of him.

"Analia, why yuh order all of dat food when yuh know yuh wouldn't be able ta eat everything?" he gently asked. I looked down at my tray.

"I don't know. I thought this would be the only time you would take us out. When Uncle Rendall brings us to McDonald's, he always buys hamburgers, French fries, and a coke. I just wanted to find out what some of the other food tasted like. Especially the shake and apple pie."

He chuckled. "Well, young lady. Yuh eyes are bigger than yuh stomach. I think yuh better stick with de smaller burgers dat Rendall does buy until yuh get a lil' older and can eat more." I agreed. "Alright, doh force yourself to eat. You can take de rest of de food home." I did as he suggested, even though I had no intention of eating any hamburgers anytime soon.

We had fun with Uncle Lloyd during the remainder of his stay. There were a few days when we didn't see him, and I'd miss him terribly. It felt good to be around someone other than Uncle Rendall, who was connected to my mother. He made us feel special and loved.

Three weeks later, he returned to Trinidad without my sister and me. I could not disguise my sadness. My lofty dreams about leaving Barbara's home were not going to come true. Instead, my Cinderella life would continue.

Chapter 33

A BUCK FIDDY

As Christmas of '73 and the first anniversary of my mother's death approached, I knew the holiday season with Barbara and Uncle Rendall would be different. No matter what, Veronica always made Christmas a joyous, festive occasion. She decorated our flat in London and the apartment on Foster Avenue beautifully. Both homes had a nice warm feeling to them, and there were plenty of presents under the tree for her family and friends. I looked at Barbara's sparsely decorated, pitiful looking artificial pine and counted six gifts.

Uncle Rendall took us to see Deborah, Sandy, Regina, Marlene, and a few more of his lady friends during the Christmas break. My sister and I came home with bags full of gifts, which made up for his and Barbara's lackluster effort.

We spent time with Aunty Lorraine over the holidays and enjoyed ourselves as usual. She and her sister, Loretta, had several gifts for us under their respective trees. I was ecstatic when I opened one of the boxes that held a new winter coat with fake beige fur around the collar and on the sleeves. Avianna got one as well. Aunty Lorraine had us stand in front of the mirror hanging on the wall in the living room while we tried them on. We looked glamorous!

I smiled as I remembered the conversation that probably led to her buying our coats. It took place about a month prior, during what had been our second visit to her apartment since my mother had died.

"Analia, where is your winter coat? It's way too cold outside to be wearing that light jacket." She was right. In the middle of winter, Avianna and I still wore windbreakers, which my godmother deemed unacceptable. I hesitated before answering.

"My winter coat doesn't fit, and Uncle Rendall won't buy me another one. He said he doesn't have any money right now. I'm going to have to wait until he gets some," I told her.

"You know what? Your uncle is full of crap! If Veronica were alive, he wouldn't pull that nonsense!"

After the Christmas holiday, I went back to my daily grind. The small amount of joy I felt around Aunty Lorraine, Deborah, and the other lovely ladies Uncle Rendall took us to visit evaporated.

We still hadn't seen or heard from my father. I didn't know if he was in London or Trinidad. I begged Uncle Rendall to find him, but he had no intention of granting my request. He had a personal agenda that did not include Victor Edmonds.

As my tenth birthday approached, I felt like an old maid. Living with Barbara and carrying out all my "adult" responsibilities had taken a toll on my psyche. I was also fed up with Uncle Rendall's disappearing act, his infrequent visits, and the lies he made me tell. But most of all, I did not appreciate the paltry sum he gave to Barbara for mine and Avianna's care, which she never failed to mention.

Life-altering events were becoming the norm for me. Another one would soon be added to my repertoire.

***

While completing my household duties, I discovered some money underneath Barbara's jewelry box. I stopped cleaning and proceeded to count the stack of tens and twenties. I held a hundred and fifty dollars in my hands.

I convinced myself that since I found the cash, I was entitled to keep it. Evidently, Barbara had forgotten about where she hid her money. Therefore, it must not have been important to her. Thoughts about what I could do with all that money swirled in my head. I decided to spend some of it and use the rest to run away with Avianna.

I went into our bedroom, got my school bag from the closet, and hid the money in an inside pocket. I resumed cleaning, finished the remainder of my duties, and spent the rest of the evening planning our great escape.

I thought I was home free when Barbara did not mention anything about the missing money the following day. All weekend long, I fantasized about what I would do while on the run.

I didn't tell Cleo about my plan to run away. However, I did let her know about the money.

"Where did you find it, Analia?" she asked with a suspicious look on her face.

"Under your mother's jewelry box. I don't think she remembers she put it there."

I told her we would shop at the Five & Dime Store to buy whatever she wanted. Cleo didn't want to spend her mother's money. But she couldn't turn down the shopping spree that I offered.

Monday morning arrived, and I went to school with a stash of cash in my bookbag, which I didn't let out of my sight for a minute. The bell indicating the end of our last period rang. I jumped out of my seat and ran to the Five & Dime store, where I planned to meet Cleo. Feeling generous, I invited a couple of my friends to go as well. I told them my uncle had given me a large allowance, and I wanted to treat them to some candy.

Cleo was already standing outside the store by the time my friends and I arrived. All of us entered and went buck wild. We grabbed Jacks, handballs, puzzles, pencils, notebooks, and candy. The store owner took the money I handed him and didn't think twice about a little girl walking around with a wad of cash in her bookbag. All that mattered was that I paid for the goods we placed on the counter by his register.

Once our shopping excursion ended, my crew and I parted ways. I planned on going straight to Aunty Lorraine's apartment, but I had two problems. First, I hadn't thought about how I would get away from Cleo after picking Avianna up from Shirley's house. Second, I didn't know my way to the Marcy Projects from our side of town. I had a lot more preparation to do, so I put my plans on hold. I got my sister from Shirley and went home.

At about five o'clock that evening, both Uncle Rendall and Barbara walked through the front door of our apartment. This was quite unusual. Barbara didn't get off from work until eleven o'clock at night, and when visiting, my uncle never showed up before seven or eight. As they passed the living where Avianna, Cleo, and I watched T.V., I said, "Hello," but neither responded.

Barbara went into the kitchen while Uncle Rendall walked towards our bedroom. When he returned, he came into the living room holding my bookbag. I began to panic as something in my gut told me he found out about the money I took from under Barbara's jewelry box.

Uncle Rendall opened my book bag, turned it upside down, and the contents, which included the remainder of the money I had not spent, spilled onto the sofa. He took a deep breath and gave me a cold, hard stare that seemed to last forever. Then he started his interrogation.

***

"Analia, where did you get all of this money, toys, and candy from?"

I heard my heart beating loudly. "A friend of mine at school gave them to me," I answered hesitantly.

"Which friend? What is her name?"

The beating of my heart now sounded like a kettle drum. "Her name is Charlotte, and she's in my homeroom class."

He took a deep breath and exhaled loudly. "She's in yuh homeroom class, huh? Analia, yuh lying? Do you think I'm stupid?" he asked. Although he spoke in a low tone, to me, he sounded deadly.

"No, Uncle Rendall," I replied in an unsteady voice. All of a sudden, Barbara appeared and sat down next to him on the sofa.

"I'm going ta ask you one more time. Where yuh get all of dis stuff from and who bought Cleopatra her toys and candy?"

"Charlotte did."

He took another deep breath and started to shake his head slowly.

"Okay, since yuh not going ta tell me de truth, I'm going ta fix yuh little ass. How old am I?" he asked.

"You're twenty-four," I replied.

"How old are you?"

"Eight." I didn't know where this line of questioning was leading to, but I'd soon find out.

"What is the difference in our ages?" he asked.

"Excuse me?"

He sucked his teeth then shouted, "Don't play stupid with me! What is de difference in our ages? How many more years older am I than you?"

I was puzzled, and the look on my face told him so.

"Analia! Subtract eight from twenty-four!" he yelled.

I did my calculation and blurted out, "Sixteen."

"Exactly. When you were born, I was sixteen years old. I've been on this earth much longer than you. I have a lot more experience than you, so you can't pull any tricks on me!"

My eyes started to water as I began to fidget nervously in my seat. My uncle's following directive confirmed what I had been thinking.

"You see that extension cord over there?" he asked while motioning at the outlet behind the T.V.

"Yes."

"Go and bring it to me."

I walked over to the outlet, unplugged the extension cord, and handed it to him. I watched as he slowly folded the cord in thirds.

"I know you found that money under Barbara's jewelry box. For your information, that was de woman's friggin' rent money. Now I have to find dat from somewhere to pay her back! Don't you ever touch anything in this house that doesn't belong to you again!" He grabbed me by the collar of my dress and began to beat me with the extension cord.

Each stroke cut into the skin on my legs. I had never been hit like that before. The beating my mother gave me with the straps from my Sunday school bag was a joke by comparison. I honestly thought I would die. I screamed and screamed until I couldn't scream anymore. Only when it seemed as though all my uncle's energy had been spent did the beating end.

"Get in the damn bed!" he shouted.

I picked myself up off the floor and adjusted my dress, which had risen during the beating. My legs felt like lead, my throat burned, and every other part of my body ached. I walked toward the bedroom, flung myself on the bed, and cried hysterically. Avianna and Cleo were listening in the bedroom to my entire interrogation and beating. They both cried as well. Cleo knew her turn was next when Uncle Rendall loudly called her name. By the time she entered the living room and stood in front of him, she was bawling.

"What yuh crying for?" Barbara yelled. "Yuh going ta get yuh blasted ass beat as well. Instead of telling me what Analia did, yuh went right along with her! Yuh just as bad as she is!"

Uncle Rendall gave Cleo two slaps on her butt with his hand, which was nothing compared to what I received, and told her to get in the bed as well. Neither of us had dinner that evening, and we both cried ourselves to sleep.

Chapter 34

THE AFTERMATH

I woke up the morning after my beating to discover bruises, welts, and a few open cuts all over my legs. When I showered, they stung and burned. I replayed each hit with the heavy extension cord over and over in my mind. I just could not believe that the uncle I had loved so dearly had given me the worst beating of my life.

Barbara remained in her bed while I got dressed. After barely eating my cereal, I left for school with Cleo without saying a word to her or the dour witch.

I took my time walking to school. I had no other choice. Had my pace been faster, I would have irritated the welts on my legs. I wore tights to cover them up; however, that was a mistake. They only worsened my discomfort. I thought I would have been late, but surprisingly, I made it to school on time.

My homeroom teacher, Mr. Solomon, was a huge man, very tall with a thick body and a huge head covered with a mop of dark brown hair. He had the uncanny ability to look angry and happy at the same time. But when he smiled, you felt an inner warmth emanate from him.

Mr. Solomon had a booming voice which he would not hesitate to raise to get our attention. Especially when the boys in our class challenged him. He kept order amongst his students but was fair. He also had a compassionate side and took a great deal of interest in the welfare of all his pupils.

I walked over to my desk and tried to sit down but paused. I was wracked with pain. The expression on my face caught Mr. Solomon's attention. He called my name and motioned for me to come to him.

"Analia, is everything okay with you?" he asked. I started crying uncontrollably in front of him and my entire class. Mr. Solomon told everyone to remain seated and asked me to go with him to the principal's office.

Once we were in the hallway, he asked me to stop. As I walked in front of him and through the open door, I could feel my teacher's eyes on my back. I hadn't realized that several of my cuts began to bleed, and the blood was seeping through my beige tights.

"Analia, stop for a minute," Mr. Solomon instructed. I did as I was told. With a look of concern, he asked, "What happened to your legs?"

I didn't want to tell him about the beating, so I lied and said I fell. Without saying a word, his eyes conveyed a message. One that said, *"I know for sure that what I'm seeing did not come from a fall."*

"Analia, you can trust me. So why don't you tell me the truth?"

I could not contain the flow of tears. Right there in the hallway, I told him about stealing Barbara's rent money to run away and the beating Uncle Rendall gave me. Mr. Solomon looked troubled. I had been a student of his for almost two years, but he had no idea about the upheaval I had experienced.

"Analia. Come with me to Mrs. Purvis' office," he instructed.

My stomach lurched. I wasn't particularly fond of our principal and was reluctant to share any details about my personal life. But when we got to her office, I figured that it would be best to go ahead and tell her everything.

I told her about my beating the night before, being separated from my father, my mother's death, and about Uncle Rendall making me live with someone who treated me like a servant. Once I finished talking, both Mr. Solomon and Mrs. Purvis looked at me in astonishment.

They ascertained that I had a close relationship with the woman called Aunty Lorraine. It seemed she would be the best person to contact to confirm what I had just told them.

Mrs. Purvis stated that she wanted to call my godmother and asked me for her number. I gladly recalled it out loud.

She looked at Mr. Solomon and asked him to take me to the nurse's office. "Tom, have Ms. Benson look at those cuts on Analia's legs. I don't like how they are bleeding."

"No problem. Are you thinking about calling BCW?" he asked her.

"I'm not sure. I think I better call the godmother first to confirm whether or not what she told us is true."

They told me to leave the room while Mrs. Purvis called Aunty Lorraine. I did not doubt that she would verify my story. Many years later, my godmother told me that Mrs. Purvis wanted to contact the Bureau of Child Welfare. She suspected that I was being abused and in peril. She felt that my living conditions with Barbara were neither in my or Avianna's best interests and that we would be better off elsewhere.

Aunty Lorraine convinced her not to contact the authorities since, more likely than not, we'd have to live with foster parents or be placed in a group home. She assured my principal, Avianna, and I could live with her and that she would find a way to work things out with my uncle.

After seeing the nurse, I returned to Mrs. Purvis' office, where I stayed for the remainder of the day. She told me to sit in one of the vacant chairs at a small round table and gave me two books to read at my leisure; Charlotte's Web and Harriet, the Spy.

"Analia, I have a few things to take care of, so I am going to be in and out of the office. If you need anything, Mrs. O'Neil will take care of you okay?"

"Okay. Thanks Mrs. Purvis."

When left alone, I'd study the maps of dried blood on my tights as flashbacks of my beating came to mind. I was nervous about the evening ahead of me.

Shortly before three o'clock, Mrs. Purvis announced that it was time for me to get ready to go home.

"Are you sure you're going to be okay? Would you like someone to walk home with you?" she asked.

My stomach felt queasy.

"That's okay Mrs. Purvis. I'll be fine."

I was surprised when she hugged me briefly and said, "Alright, young lady. I'll see you tomorrow."

The bell rang, and I left to meet Cleo. I usually made it to her school by 3:15 pm at the latest. However, this afternoon, I took my sweet time and got there at 3:35 pm. I was in no rush to return to our house of horrors. Cleo and I walked home in silence.

When we arrived, Barbara was there. I greeted her and went

straight to our bedroom to change into my house clothes. I removed my blood-stained tights with care, wincing as I peeled them off some of the scabs they had stuck to. Then, I put them in the old pillowcase we used for a laundry bag.

I sat on the bed and looked around the room as if seeing everything for the first time. I studied the carpet, our dresser, the ceiling, curtains, and single window. I wasn't particularly interested in these objects. I just didn't want to go into the living room and was buying some time. I felt weird, like an outcast.

Barbara left the apartment without saying a word to Cleo or me. When she returned, she had Avianna with her. Uncle Rendall showed up a few minutes afterward. He peeked in the bedroom and spoke directly to Cleo and Avianna but didn't say anything to me.

I lay down on the bed, and again, my thoughts drifted to my beating. Eventually, I took a shower, bid everyone goodnight, and went to bed. As with the prior evening, I did not eat dinner.

The next day started pretty normally, except that Barbara was home and made us breakfast. She dressed Avianna and stated that she would take her to the babysitter instead of me. At school, Mr. Solomon conducted his classroom activities as usual, but he asked me to stay behind for a minute when the bell rang.

"How are things at home Analia? Are your uncle and aunt treating you and your sister okay?"

I looked around the room before answering. "We're doing good."

Mr. Solomon smiled. "As long as you are alright, that's what matters. If anything changes, you let me know, okay?"

I never saw him again.

Chapter 35

HASTY DEPARTURE

Much later that night, after we retired for bed, I woke up to see Barbara shuffling through the closet that I shared with Cleo and Avianna. Thinking she was just rearranging our clothes, I drifted back to sleep.

The following morning, I awoke to find Barbara and Uncle Rendall at the kitchen table talking. As I approached the bathroom to shower, he motioned for me to come into the kitchen.

"Sit down for a minute. I need ta talk with you." I listened with trepidation as he told me about his plans for my bright future.

"Ever since you have been living here, Barbara and I have tried ta do everything possible ta take care of you an' Avianna. Since it is obvious that you neither appreciate what we try ta do, I think you should go an' live with yuh grandmother in England. You'll be leaving today."

This was the best news I had heard in a long time. I was going back home, and even though Granny and I were not close, I had to be better off living with her. The only problem with this scenario was that Avianna would not be going with me. I couldn't stand the thought of leaving her, but that decision was out of my hands.

Barbara and Uncle Rendall decided to take Cleo to school and Avianna to the babysitter. I hugged my baby sister tightly and told her I loved her. Avianna didn't have a clue about what was going on and just went with the program. Uncle Rendall told me to stay home, get dressed, and wait for him to return. While they were gone, I seized the opportunity to call Aunty Lorraine.

"Your uncle said what?" she screamed when I relayed the conversation that I had with him a short time before.

"Aunty Lorraine, he said I have to go to England today. I think my flight is this afternoon. Do you think I'll be able to see you before I leave?" I asked.

I heard my godmother begin to cry on the other end of the line. "I can't believe your uncle is so vindictive! Veronica would kick his ass if she were alive to see what he is doing to her daughters! Analia, I'll be over there in a few minutes; I'm leaving right now!"

I urged her to hurry as I didn't think we had much time left.

I got dressed and wandered through the apartment, not sure what to do with myself. I saw an open suitcase filled with my belongings on the living room floor. It dawned on me that Barbara had been packing my things for my "surprise" trip during the previous night.

Uncle Rendall finally returned, but Barbara did not. He made a few phone calls and spoke to everyone in a hushed tone. About half an hour later, he told me we were leaving for the airport and that I should get my coat. I wasn't going to see my godmother after all.

We left the apartment and walked a few steps to his car. He put my suitcase in the trunk, and just as he was getting ready to open the passenger door to let me in, Aunty Lorraine pulled up in her Grand Prix. He turned towards me and rolled his eyes.

She got out of her car and ran towards my uncle's vehicle.

"Rendall! Wait a minute! What the hell are you doing? Why are you sending Analia away?" she yelled.

He sucked his teeth. "Lorraine, stop with the noise already. It'll be better for everyone if Analia lives with my mother," he replied.

"Better for who? Why are you separating her from Avianna? You know damn well that Veronica wouldn't want that, Rendall. Please don't send her away. I'll do what you want me to do, but please don't send my baby away!" she cried.

She grabbed Uncle Rendall's arm and asked him over and over not to send me to England. When she realized that he would not change his mind, she started crying uncontrollably. What a pitiful sight! Her nose ran while her beautiful light brown eyes turned red. Seeing her that upset got to me, but I didn't cry. My tears dried up on the night of my ass whipping.

Uncle Rendall told her she could come to the airport with us but had to stop "with all a dat crying."

"Oh shut the hell up! You can't tell me what to do. You know how much I love her, and you're taking her away from me. You make me sick!" she shouted.

Despite what she had just declared, she parked her car, got in his, and rode with us to John F. Kennedy Airport. We sat together in the backseat. She hugged me and cried during the entire ride.

When we arrived at the airport, Uncle Rendall checked me in. The ticket agent gave me a pouch containing a piece of paper with my name and Granny's contact information. Then, the three of us walked over to the waiting area and sat down until it was time for me to board.

I knew Aunty Lorraine's telephone number by rote. However, she still wanted me to write it down in the small spiral notebook I had in my bookbag. She also gave me the telephone numbers and addresses of her sisters, in case I could not get in touch with her.

Uncle Rendall didn't say one word to me.

Not too long afterward, a flight attendant came over to where we were sitting and told my uncle she was ready to take me on board. I kissed Aunty Lorraine for the last time, mumbled good-bye to Uncle Rendall, and walked off with the attendant.

So many emotions ran through me as I sat on the plane waiting for us to depart. I was sad, excited, happy, and anxious all at once. I was getting away from a life of burden with Barbara but sad about leaving Avianna and my godmother behind. Little did I know that I was jumping from the frying pan into the fire. Living with Barbara couldn't come close to the life of hell that I would experience with my grandmother, Clarinda Walton.

To Be Continued…

Part 1

BOOK CLUB QUESTIONS

What did you like about Part I of this story? What didn't you like?

_____

_____

_____

_____

What has stuck with you the most?

_____

_____

_____

_____

Was there a situation or event that reminded you about your own life? What feelings did it evoke?

_____

_____

_____

_____

Neither of Analia's parents spoke to her about their move to America. Given the life altering change that was about to take place, do you think this was appropriate? If not, why?

_____

_____

_____

_____

If you were separated from your spouse, would you discuss the state of your marriage with your child?

_____

_____

_____

_____

Was there a better way for Analia's mother to introduce her to Alex?

_____

_____

_____

_____

If you are a product of separation or divorce and your parents have new partners, how did you feel upon meeting them? Were you blindsided?

_____

_____

_____

_____

Why do you think Analia never told her mother about the incident with Alex? Do you think Veronica would have believed her?

_____

_____

_____

_____

What stands out most to you about Rendall Walton?

_____

_____

_____

_____

If you have suffered the loss of a parent at an early age, how did the other adults in your life help you to adjust? Is there something that you wish they would have done differently?

_____

_____

_____

_____

Analia's father abandoned her and her sister when they needed him most. What are your thoughts about his actions?

_____

_____

_____

_____

Are there any takeaways that have prompted you to think differently about certain matters going forward?

_____

_____

_____

_____

What burning question do you have for the author?

_____

_____

_____

_____

Made in the USA
Coppell, TX
14 November 2021